Lotsa Lists!

SKETCH & DESIGN

- ☐ Tattoo Creator
- ☐ Scrolling Script Writing
- ☐ Dolphin's Design—a—Dress
- ☐ Gingerbread Cookies
- ☐ Daisy's Pizza
- ☐ Burger, Shake And Fries
- ☐ Toffee Apple
- ☐ Bunny Biscuit
- ☐ Chaise Longue
- ☐ Ornate Mirror
- ☐ Retro Telephone
- ☐ Crystal Chandelier
- ☐ Luxury Bed
- ☐ Exotic Flowers
- ☐ Nick's Picture Prompt
- ☐ Copy Queenie

QUIZZES & GAMES

- ☐ JW Mate Match Quiz
- ☑ Character Selector
- ☑ Destiny's Drama Queen Quiz
- ☐ Find Tracy's Photo
- ☐ Discover Your Gem Destiny
- ☐ What's Your Fear Factor?
- ☐ Could You Be The Next JW?
- ☐ Carnival of Luck
- ☐ Are You Marty or Melissa?
- ☐ Tracy's True or False!
- ☐ Victorian Parlour Party
- ☐ What Happens Next?
- ☐ JW X Factor
- ☐ The Xylophone Test
- ☐ Marigold's Zodiac Storyteller
- ☐ Lizzie Zipmouth's Puzzle Page
- ☐ Tracy's Do or Discuss

MAKES & BAKES

- ☐ Bestie Button Bracelets
- ☐ Spooky Balloons
- ☐ Valentine Makes
- ☐ Butterfly Feeder
- ☐ Lucky Dice Nails
- ☐ Marty & Melissa T—shirts
- ☐ Fairy Bakes
- ☐ Beauty's Birthday Biscuits

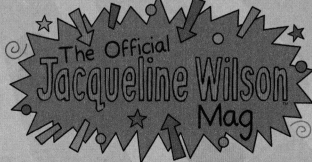

The Official Jacqueline Wilson Mag

Pick 3!

My three favourite things in this book are —

1 ....

2 ....

Hi Everyone

It's Annual time again — and this is a special bumper one too! It should keep you going for weeks. It features all my very favourite stories too. I have a particular soft spot for *The Illustrated Mum*. I got the idea for this story when my daughter Emma and I were having a marvellous holiday in New York. We'd spent an exciting day shopping and going to art galleries, and were having a rest and an ice-cream in Central Park. It's a wonderful place for people watching. We saw an amazing woman with many decorative tattoos walking along with two little girls in dressing up clothes, staggering a little in their borrowed high heels. When they'd passed us Emma whispered, 'They look exactly like characters in one of your books!' 'Maybe I'll write about them one day,' I said, and I jotted a little note about them in my diary. That was how I came up with the idea for *The Illustrated Mum*, the story of two sisters, Dolphin and Star, and their mother, Marigold. I do hope you'll enjoy inventing a new tattoo for Marigold and designing a special dress for Dolphin. I think I'll have a go myself.

I'm an only child but I've always wished I had a sister. It would be especially interesting to have a twin sister. Did you enjoy finding out what happened to identical twins Ruby and Garnet in my book *The Butterfly Club*? They star in *Double Act*, a story that they take turns writing. You'll be able to read about their cringes in a special feature in the Annual.

I think the saddest of all my stories is probably *My Sister Jodie*. I know it's made a lot of girls cry — but they always say they ENJOY having a good weep at a story. I'm not sure how I'd get on with a wild older sister like Jodie. She'd be great fun but I'd get very worried about her most of the time. There's a super-spooky Jodie Halloween section inside. I always find Halloween a bit of a challenge because so many children come knocking at my door and I have to hang on tight to my puppy Jackson each time in case he escapes.

Children often ask me who my favourite character in all my books is. I nearly always choose Hetty Feather. She loves writing and making up stories — and you'll have an opportunity to help her inside. There are so many more fun features in the annual that I can't list them all. Why not flick through the pages and see for yourself?

Have a great time!

Jacqueline Wilson
xxx

Personalise It YOUR Way!

A IS FOR ALL ABOUT AMAZING ME!

Meet Me!

Real name ..... ReBecca
What I wish my name was! ..... Lillian

Age ..... 10 years old

Draw a doodle of yourself here!

My JW Match!

Pick the JW character you're most like!

☐ Melissa   ☐ Elsa   ☐ Beauty

3 Things I ♥ About ME!
(Don't be shy!)

1. I'm kind

2. I'm nice

3. I'm the best friend ever

☐ Tracy   ☐ Gemma   ☐ Hetty

5

My Favourites!

COLOUR ... Blue

BOOK ... Katy

SONG ... Say some thing, I beauty lost cuz... Michael

SUBJECT ... Reading English

FILM ...

WEBSITE ... YouTube

3 things that make me happy:

1. FAMILY

2. Drawing

3. Reading

Pick me!

Would you rather...

Eat stinky blue cheese OR sniff your bro's smelly socks?

Jump into a pool filled with melted chocolate OR gummi bears?

Have angel wings OR a mermaid's tail?

No, choose me!

Be friends with Jacky OR mates with Nick?

Ride a dragon OR a unicorn?

Watch the same TV programme OR read the same book for a whole week?

I ♥ My Bestie!

BF's name ....

Our fave thing to do together ....

....

....

Three things I love about my BF:

1. ....

2. ....

3. ....

When I grow up I want to be:

_____

_____

_____

because _____

_____

_____

Friends Forever!

Draw you and your bestie here! Style yourselves silly, or design totally fashionable outfits — you decide!

miss Ally + MrStudent
=
BFF

Now turn over to find out which JW friendship pair you and your BF are most like!

B IS FOR BEST FRIENDS

WHICH JW BEST FRIENDS ARE YOU MOST LIKE?

What to do:

Get together with your BF, read each question and tick the answers that sound most like your friendship!

1 Choose your fave sleepover activity:

- [ ] Karaoke!
- [ ] Making gifts for each other.
- [x] Sharing secrets.

2 The two of you make a brilliant team. You're best at...

- [x] Dancing! Your routines are legendary.
- [ ] Crafting and baking. Especially baking, mmmm...
- [x] Creating cool clubs!

3 How many times a day do you text each other?

- [ ] 1–3 [x] 4+ [ ] None

4 Be honest — have you ever spilled your bestie's secret?

- [x] No, never!
- [ ] Just once, accidentally!
- [ ] Um, once or twice...

Alice's DIARY

5 You share a love of:

- [ ] Animals and nature.
- [ ] Dressing up and putting on a show!
- [x] Being with your BF — awww!

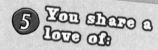

6 You overhear someone saying nasty things about your BF. You...

- [x] Tell your BF straight away. You'd never keep anything from her.
- [x] Confront the person and tell them to stop.
- [ ] Keep it to yourself to spare your bestie's feelings.

7 Pick your dream day trip...

- [x] The cinema.
- [ ] The circus.
- [ ] The zoo.

TANGLEFIELD'S CIRCUS

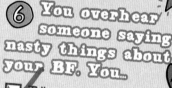
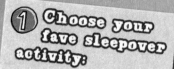

Mostly Blue

YOU ARE GEMMA AND ALICE

Best friends, through and through! You're so close, you're more like twins than BFs! You like a lot of the same things (and even share the same dislikes!) and you never grow tired of each other. Besties for life!

Mostly Orange

YOU ARE TINA AND SELMA

You have very different personalities but you work well together, despite the odd fall-out or bickering match! Whether it's creating a joint project in school or planning a sleepover, the two of you are the ultimate team!

Mostly Pink

YOU ARE HETTY AND DIAMOND

You have a friendship filled with fun and imagination! Together you enjoy performing and making people smile and laugh — perhaps you're destined for a life on stage, just like Hetty and Diamond!

BESTIE BUTTON BANDS

Make one for each of your friends!

You'll need:
- COLOURED BUTTONS
- SCISSORS
- PAPER STRING OR TWINE

1. Cut two lengths of paper string, each one around 30cm long. Take one length and thread both ends through two button holes, as shown in the picture.

2. Take the two ends and pull them through the loop to create a slip knot. Do the same for the other side of the button.

3. Wrap round your bestie's wrist and tie the four loose ends together to fasten.

Have fun making a whole stack of bracelets in different colours!

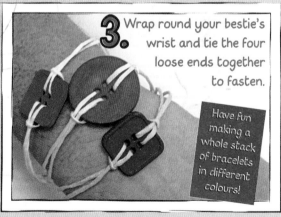

BUTTON COLOUR CHARMS!

Which ones will YOU choose?

Pink — Friends Forever
Yellow — Lots of LOLs!
Purple — Love & Loyalty
Green — Trust & Honesty
Blue — Tons of Fun!

10 Books I Love!

Have you read any of my favourite books?

1 **Nancy and Plum by Betty MacDonald.**
I must have read this story about two orphaned sisters at least twenty times when I was a child.

2 **Ballet Shoes by Noel Streatfeild.**
A lovely story about three sisters, Pauline, Petrova and Posy, who go to stage school.

3 **Little Women by Louisa M. Alcott.**
This family story might have been written long ago, but the four March sisters still seem gloriously real. Tomboy writer Jo is my favourite.

4 **What Katy Did by Susan Coolidge.**
Katy is a tomboy too, and very naughty, but then she has a terrible accident... I've written a modern version of this book!

5 **Mary Poppins by P.L.Travers.**
Everyone knows about the magical children's nanny Mary Poppins, but the books are even better than the film.

6 **Five Children and It by E. Nesbit.**
A very funny story about a family of Edwardian children who find a bad-tempered magical creature who is occasionally persuaded to grant them wishes. I've written a modern version of this book too!

7 **Marianne Dreams by Catherine Storr.**
This is a haunting story about a girl who draws a strange scary place and then dreams that she's trapped there.

8 **The Family from One End Street by Eve Garnett.**
This is the book about a really poor but lively family. I totally identified with the second sister Kate. I love the illustrations as well as the story.

 FOR OLDER READERS

9 **I Capture the Castle by Dodie Smith.**
This is a fictional diary kept by Cassandra, who lives in a tumbledown castle. I love the way the story starts!

10 **The Diary of Anne Frank by Anne Frank.**
A real diary written by a young girl who had to go into hiding during World War II. This book meant the world to me when I was growing up.

 10

 Which of these books do you think you'd like to read most?

 I CAPTURE THE CASTLE

 NANCY AND PLUM

LITTLE WOMEN

FIVE CHILDREN AND IT

THE FAMILY FROM ONE END STREET

WHAT KATY DID

MARY POPPINS

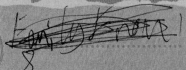 BALLET SHOES

THE DIARY OF ANNE FRANK

MARIANNE DREAMS

Character Selector!

C IS FOR CHARACTERS

2308 03   2+3+8+5

HAIR

Close your eyes and place your finger somewhere on this section. Whichever duck your finger is closest to reveals your character's hair colour!

Blonde   **Pink**   **Blue**   **Red**

Brown   **Black**   **Green**

EYE COLOUR

Do the same again in this section — the butterfly your finger lands closest to reveals your character's eye colour!

   **Brown**

2+5+0+5+2+0+0+5=20

Blue   **Green**

   Hazel

   **Grey**   Amber

PERSONALITY

What's your character like as a person? Find out here!

23 08 2005   2+3+0+

Add up all the numbers in your birthday till you're left with a single number. For example, you were born on October 12th, 2006:
12/10/2006
1+2+1+0+2+0+0+6 = 12
1+2 = 3
Your mystic number is 3!

1 **Strange, imaginative and private**
2 **Suspicious, touchy and orderly**
3 **Bold, brave and tough**
4 **Wild, supportive and happy**
5 **Shy, modest and friendly**
6 **Disorganised, lively and easy-going**
7 **Independent, trusting and relaxed**
8 **Rebellious, sensitive and feisty**
9 **Confident, practical and calm**

TURN OVER FOR MORE!

11

NAME

Now find your character's name by picking your birth day and birth month!

BIRTH DAY

1) MILLICENT
2) KRISTINA
3) SUZETTE
4) HOLLIE
5) FRANCESCA
6) BERNADETTE
7) SUKI
8) GERALDINE
9) ARAMINTA
10) MELODY
11) ELOUISE
12) LAILA
13) ROSETTA
14) CHARLISE
15) VERONICA
16) IMOGEN

17) POLLY
18) AGATHA
19) NERISSA
20) JODIE
21) OLIVE
22) EDIE
23) TABITHA
24) DOROTHEA
25) EVELYN
26) ANIKA
27) EMILIA
28) PENELOPE
29) FLORRIE
30) AILSA
31) MARNIE

BIRTH MONTH

JANUARY — Montgomery
FEBRUARY — Caldicot
MARCH — Armstrong
APRIL — Kingsley
MAY — Muircroft
JUNE — Huntington
JULY — Charlton
AUGUST — Smythson
SEPTEMBER — Dandridge
OCTOBER — Vanderbilt
NOVEMBER — Godfrey
DECEMBER — Caulfield

My character's name is Geraldine Muircroft!

GOODIE OR BADDIE?

Flip a coin to find out if your character is a goodie or a baddie!

HEADS – goodie
TAILS – baddie

FUN FACT!

Pick your favourite colour to find out something interesting about your character!

Your character is...

The eldest of 17 children!

Fluent in three languages!

Secretly scared of the dark!

A crime-fighting superhero by night!

Super-rich — but no one else knows!

Able to breathe under water!

100 years old!

A champion dog trainer!

Sketch your character HERE!

Maybe your character has an angry expression or perhaps they're super-smiley!

What kind of clothes will your character wear?

Smart or casual, trendy or boring?

Is their hair neat and tidy or wild and wacky?

Why not stick on some paper or fabric scraps to bring your character to life?

Are they big or small?

Does your character have a pet? You could draw them, too!

You could add a speech bubble with a catchphrase they always say!

Name: ....

D IS FOR DRAMA

Destiny's Drama Queen Quiz!

Colour in the stars for each answer, then add up your score!

Oh-So-Me! Pick the statement that suits your personality!

YOU LIKE TO BE...
The centre of attention!
Part of the crowd.

YOU WOULD...
Go to school with a runny nose.
Want to stay in bed for a week!

YOU DON'T LIKE...
Being in charge.
Being ignored!

GOSSIP ALERT!
It's already old news!
You're the last to know!

YOU WOULD...
Keep a secret.
Tell a mate!

  Pick five words that describe you best!

HAPPY

CONFIDENT

THOUGHTFUL

FUN

SILLY

MOTIVATED

LOYAL

TALENTED

SHY

UNPREDICTABLE

The Character Circle!

Circle the answer that's most like you in each segment, then add up your scores!

YOUR FAVE SCHOOL SUBJECT IS —
English
Music
Art

Writing Stories
Music

YOU'RE MOST LIKE —
Sunset
Sweetie
Destiny

YOUR FAVE NEW PET IS —
Arti
Jacob
Jackson

Have You Ever?

Your drama queen confessions — choose yes or no!

Have you ever let someone take the blame for something you did?
YES NO

Have you ever made up a story about someone?
YES NO

Have you ever entered a talent show?
YES
NO

Have you ever started an argument?
YES NO

Have you ever had a tantrum when you've left something?
YES NO

NOW ADD UP YOUR STARS...

Get Your Drama Queen Rating!

20-30 Stars
You're not always the centre of attention but that's how you like it! You haven't quite reached royalty on our drama queen rating yet, but that won't stop you reaching stardom!

40-50 Stars
Wow! There's nothing shy about you... you are a Drama Diva! You love having as much excitement in your life as possible — even if that does mean it can get a bit dramatic at times!

15

Let's write a new ending together!

Write A Dramatic Ending!

People often talk about the importance of having a good, interesting beginning to a story. I think you definitely need to have a good ending. It's always so tempting to rush things in a few skimpy sentences because you're so eager to finish your story! Try hard to build to a really exciting, dramatic end of your story. It doesn't have to end happily ever after, but everything should be resolved. I think my most dramatic ending was in *My Sister Jodie*. It even took me by surprise!

Sometimes it can be hard to write a perfect ending and you may have to try out a few different ones. Pick one of my stories below and think about these questions before writing a new, super dramatic ending!

- Will my main character do something unexpected?
- How will the end of the story affect the other characters in the book?
- Do I want my story to have a happy or sad ending?

Think about what would happen if Floss went to visit her mum in Australia!

Does disaster strike when Sunset sends Destiny tickets to a VIP party?

What would have happened if Dan hadn't shown up to the party in time?

JACQUELINE WILSON
CHILDREN'S LAUREATE 2005 - 2007
CANDYFLOSS
NICK SHARRATT

Jacqueline Wilson
GIRLS IN LOVE
Illustrated by Nick Sharratt

Jacqueline Wilson
LITTLE DARLINGS
FRIENDSHIP
DESTINY SUNSET

Extreme ENEMIES!

E IS FOR ENEMIES

Tracy Vs Justine

Mean Girl Moments:

- When she reads out Tracy's life book in a silly baby voice.
- She goes off with Tracy's best friend Louise.
- She dares Tracy to eat TWO wriggly worms. Bleurgh!

Worst Moment:

- When Tracy gets hauled off to the quiet room after she hits Justine. Uh—oh.

Best Moment:

- When Tracy keeps her cool and doesn't react to Justine's teasing because she really wants to go on her lunch date with Cam.

ENEMY RATING: 4/5

Mandy Vs Kim

Mean Girl Moments:

- She's nasty about Mandy's mum.
- She laughs at Mandy's bunny knickers.
- She gangs up on Mandy in the girls' toilets.

Worst Moment:

- When Kim tells a big, nasty lie and says that Mandy hit her!

Best Moment:

- When Tanya stands up to the bullies and they all just scuttle off without as much as a peep. She even calls them 'little girlies'!

ENEMY RATING: 3/5

Floss Vs Rihannon

Mean Girl Moments:

- She calls Floss Smelly Chip.
- She holds her nose whenever Floss moves.
- She tells everyone that Floss's mum has left forever and ever.

Worst Moment:

- When Rihannon tells Floss that her mum wants to phone social services.

Best Moment:

- When Floss tells her she doesn't want to be friends with her — she wants to hang out with Susan instead! Hooray!

ENEMY RATING: 5/5

Find Tracy's Photo!

Oh no — stinky Justine has hidden Tracy's precious photo of her mum! What a meanie! Can you solve the puzzles to fill in the boxes at the end and help her find it before TB throws a massive wobbly?

Grrrrr! I'll get my revenge — don't you worry!

Tracy Feels...

Cross out the letters that appear more than once to reveal how Tracy feels when she realises the photo is missing...

OIQLATNLTQILGRYIO

A n g r y

Put the second letter in the second box.

Eye Spy!

Who saw Justine sneaking away with the photo? Fill in the missing letter on each line to make two brand new words. The name of the person will appear in the boxes!

Dri **b** ush
Orang **e** arth
Fee **t** oe
Tre **l** normous
Tige **r** abbit

Put the second letter in the tenth box.
Put the third letter in the sixth box.
Put the fourth letter in the eighth box.

Hide & Seek!

Which room in The Dumping Ground has Justine put the photo?

My first is in bike but not in hike.
My second is in egg and also in apple
My third is the first in dinosaur
My fourth is in run but not in fun
My fifth is in so but not in sew
My sixth is the second in toad
My seventh is in mouse but not in house

___ ___ ___ ___ ___ ___ ___

Put the first letter in the ninth box. Put the second letter in the fourth box. Put the fourth letter in the fifth box.

Word Scramble!

Unscramble the letters to finally reveal where the photo is!

RLUCY
Clue: Tracy's hair isn't straight — it's _____
Put the second letter in the first box.

HAMING
Clue: Peter's second name is _____
Put the fourth letter in the seventh box.

LLWOODYHO _____
Clue: Tracy pretends that her mum is an actress here.
Put the ninth letter in the third and eleventh boxes.

I'm on to you Justine!

1.	2.	3.	4.	5.	6.	7.	8.	9.	10.	11.
u	n	d	e	c		t	h	e	l	b	e	d

Speedy Sketches!

Floss's Toffee Apple

Why not stick some red glitter to Floss's toffee apple? Mmmm!

1.
2.
3.

Beauty's Bunny Biscuits

Use a slightly darker shade to colour the outline to give your bunny biscuits a 3D effect!

1.
2.
3.

Jacky's books are filled with scrummy-licious descriptions of food! I'm getting hungry just thinking about them...

Draw Your Dream Dinner!

Would it be...

A towering dessert with lashings of cream and chocolate — dessert for dinner rules!

A sophisticated 10-course banquet, of course! You've always wanted to try caviar, *darling*...

Eggs, sausage and beans — breakfast is the most important meal of the day, so you should get to have it twice!

Draw your yummiest concoction here

I'd pick a chicken dish, followed by a gooseberry crumble and cream for pudding!

F IS FOR FOOD

Fairy Bakes!

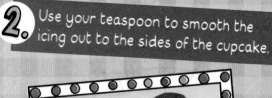

These forest fairy cakes are delicious!

You'll need:
- Sponge cupcakes
- Red food colouring
- 125g icing sugar
- White chocolate drops
- Lollypop stick

1. Mix 125g icing sugar with 1 tsp of food colouring in the bowl. The more food colouring you add, the brighter your icing will be! Carefully hold the cupcake upside down over the bowl and dip into the icing until the entire top of the cupcake is covered. Allow any excess icing to drizzle back into the bowl.

Wash any excess red colouring off your hands!

2. Use your teaspoon to smooth the icing out to the sides of the cupcake.

3. Take a white chocolate drop and press it into the icing with the stick, so that the pointy part is being pushed toward the sponge.

4. Place your finished cupcakes in the fridge until the icing hardens — then enjoy!

Turn to P83 to cut out some fairy cake toppers!

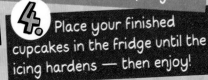

JACKY'S GEM GIRLS

G IS FOR GEMS

I like to call my fictional girls interesting names. I'm very fond of jewellery, so it's not surprising that I often choose gems as names!

When I wrote about identical twins in *Double Act* I called them Ruby and Garnet as they're both similar red stones. Hetty Feather has got not one but two alternative gem names, Sapphire Battersea and Emerald Star, and her little circus friend is called Diamond. Then there's Opal Plumstead, of course. I've just bought a new ring with a lemon quartz gemstone. Lemon Quartz sounds a perfect name for a storybook character...

Jacqueline Wilson — Double Act
Jacqueline Wilson — SAPPHIRE BATTERSEA
Jacqueline Wilson — EMERALD STAR
Jacqueline Wilson — DIAMOND
Jacqueline Wilson — OPAL PLUMSTEAD
Jacqueline Wilson — MY SISTER JODIE

Do You Know?
Which of Jacky's books Jade appears in?

Why Don't You?
Design a character called Lemon Quartz!

Find Your Gem Name

Match the day you were born on to reveal a glittering new name!

☆ MONDAY — Emerald Austen
TUESDAY — Topaz Jones
WEDNESDAY — Amethyst Updike
THURSDAY — Ruby Starshine
FRIDAY — Onyx Osbourne
SATURDAY — Diamond Thorne
SUNDAY — Sapphire Spinel

My gem name is Emerald Austen!

WHY NOT?
Use your gem name as your author name!

23

Reveal Your Gem Destiny

Unlock the secrets of the stones!

JANUARY GARNET

GEM POWER:
- MONEY
- LUCK
- LOVE

YOU ARE:
- POSITIVE
- CREATIVE
- LOYAL

YOUR GEM JOBS:
- ARTIST
- WRITER
- EDITOR

LUCKY GEM NUMBER

FEBRUARY AMETHYST

GEM POWER:
- HEALTH
- PATIENCE
- CALM

YOU ARE:
- GENEROUS
- KIND
- RELAXED

YOUR GEM JOBS:
- PARAMEDIC
- VET
- MARINE BIOLOGIST

LUCKY GEM NUMBER

MARCH AQUAMARINE

GEM POWER:
- PEACE
- PROTECTION
- HAPPINESS

YOU ARE:
- CONFIDENT
- FEARLESS
- FEISTY

YOUR GEM JOBS:
- YOUTUBER
- LECTURER
- POLITICIAN

LUCKY GEM NUMBER

APRIL DIAMOND

GEM POWER:
- PROTECTION
- LOVE
- ENERGY

YOU ARE:
- A LEADER
- DEPENDABLE
- STRONG

YOUR GEM JOBS:
- LAWYER
- DOCTOR
- MANAGER

LUCKY GEM NUMBER

MAY EMERALD

GEM POWER:
- LOVE
- SUCCESS
- GOOD JUDGEMENT

YOU ARE:
- HAPPY
- HELPFUL
- FRIENDLY

YOUR GEM JOBS:
- DOCTOR
- OPTICIAN
- COMPANY OWNER

LUCKY GEM NUMBER

JUNE PEARL

GEM POWER:
- SUCCESS
- CONCENTRATION
- CHARITY

YOU ARE:
- HONEST
- WISE
- DEDICATED

YOUR GEM JOBS:
- TEACHER
- ANIMAL CARER
- GARDEN DESIGNER

LUCKY GEM NUMBER

JULY RUBY

GEM POWER:
- FRIENDSHIP
- LOVE
- FIRE

YOU ARE:
- CLEVER
- DETERMINED
- BRAVE

YOUR GEM JOBS:
- DESIGNER
- DETECTIVE
- MUSEUM CURATOR

LUCKY GEM NUMBER

AUGUST PERIDOT

GEM POWER:
- MONEY
- POSITIVITY
- FRIENDSHIP

YOU ARE:
- HAPPY
- CARING
- RELAXED

YOUR GEM JOBS:
- VET
- DENTIST
- ANIMAL EXPERT

LUCKY GEM NUMBER

SEPTEMBER SAPPHIRE

GEM POWER:
- JOY
- PEACE
- BEAUTY

YOU ARE:
- TRUTHFUL
- DEVOTED
- SINCERE

YOUR GEM JOBS:
- JUDGE
- JOURNALIST
- ECOLOGIST

LUCKY GEM NUMBER

OCTOBER OPAL

GEM POWER:
- INSPIRATION
- IMAGINATION
- SPIRIT

YOU ARE:
- LOYAL
- FIERY
- FUN

YOUR GEM JOBS:
- CHEF
- CELEB STYLIST
- SCIENTIST

LUCKY GEM NUMBER

NOVEMBER YELLOW CITRINE

GEM POWER:
- SUCCESS
- HAPPINESS
- ENERGY

YOU ARE:
- CONFIDENT
- LIVELY
- CREATIVE

YOUR GEM JOBS:
- LAWYER
- ARTIST
- BOOK EDITOR

LUCKY GEM NUMBER

DECEMBER TOPAZ

GEM POWER:
- CONFIDENCE
- FORTUNE
- PROTECTION

YOU ARE:
- CREATIVE
- IMAGINATIVE
- UNIQUE

YOUR GEM JOBS:
- FASHION DESIGNER
- WRITER
- ARCHITECT

LUCKY GEM NUMBER

GEM LUCK!

Work out your lucky gem number! Here's how —

⭐ Match the letters of your birth stone to the code.

⭐ Add the numbers together and then add your birth month. Now add the totals together.

⭐ Now keep adding the digits till you get a number that's 10 or less.

FOR EXAMPLE:
RUBY: 18 + 21 + 2 + 25 = 66
JULY: 7

ADD THE TOTALS: 66 + 7 = 73
ADD THE DIGITS: 7 + 3 = 10
(add again if your total is more than 10)
YOUR GEM NUMBER IS 10

A	B	C	D	E	F	G	H	I	J	K	L	M
1	2	3	4	5	6	7	8	9	10	11	12	13

N	O	P	Q	R	S	T	U	V	W	X	Y	Z
14	15	16	17	18	19	20	21	22	23	24	25	26

GEM SECRETS!

Match your lucky gem number to reveal a secret —

1 Don't make an enemy out of someone you meet.

2 Wear your birthstone for extra luck.

3 Don't turn down an invite you receive.

4 A new style you try will work out well!

5 Spend your pocket money wisely!

6 A friend needs someone to share her troubles.

7 Pay attention to details for more success.

8 A friend is feeling left out, take care not to ignore her.

9 Too much chatting could land you in trouble!

10 Don't believe everything you hear!

GEM COLOUR CODE

What are the shades of the stones telling?

GREEN
HEALTH
PEACE
A CLEAR MIND

RED
EXCITEMENT
CONFIDENCE
LEADERSHIP

WHITE
HOPE
GOODNESS
LIGHT

DEEP BLUE
STRENGTH
TRUST
SUCCESS

PURPLE
CREATIVE
ORIGINAL
WISE

YELLOW
FRIENDLY
WARM
OPTIMISTIC

PINK
SENSITIVE
LOYAL
BEAUTY

BLUE
SPIRIT
AMBITION
DETERMINATION

What's Your FEAR FACTOR?

Are you as brave and bold as me?

AN ODD WAILING SOUND IS COMING FROM THE ATTIC! YOU...

- ☐ Grab your torch and head on up there to investigate.
- ☐ Call the police. And the fire brigade, the coastguard, your neighbour's sister's friend...
- ☑ Ask your dad to check it out. Well, that's his job, right?

YOUR BF PUTS ON A SCARY MOVIE AT A SLEEPOVER. YOU...

- ☑ Watch parts of it through the gaps in your fingers — eek!
- ☐ Turn up the volume and sit as close to the telly as possible so you don't miss a thing.
- ☐ Take the DVD, open the bedroom window and throw it out. Sorted!

IT'S LATE AT NIGHT WHEN YOU SPOT A GLOWING LIGHT OUTSIDE. YOU...

- ☐ Hide under your bed and stay there all night.
- ☑ Peep out your window. Phew, it's only the neighbour's security light.
- ☐ Hope that it's aliens, coming to abduct you. Maybe they'll make you their leader!

YOUR BRO JUMPS OUT AT YOU IN THE MIDDLE OF THE NIGHT! YOU...

- ☐ Devise the ultimate plan for revenge! You'll make him pay...
- ☐ Drop to the floor in a faint.
- ☑ Laugh in his face. Brothers are s-o-o-o lame!

A HUGE SPIDER HAS BUILT A WEB IN THE CORNER OF YOUR ROOM! YOU...

- ☑ Move out. Immediately.
- ☐ Send in a trained specialist (um, Dad) to remove the hairy fiend.
- ☐ Ask if you can keep it for a pet.

MOSTLY ORANGE

SUPER SCARED!
Honestly, you're just like my sister, Pearl — a total wimp! You wouldn't catch me shrieking over a tiny spider or a harmless little ghost!

MOSTLY PINK

OH-SO-CAUTIOUS
You're pretty sensible and level-headed, just like Harley! What's more, you're not afraid to ask for help when you need it. Bravo!

MOSTLY PURPLE

FANTASTICALLY FEARLESS!
There's not a lot in this world that would scare you! You're always looking for that next big adventure in life, just like me! Wanna be friends?

SPOOKY STORY STARTER!

Play along to find a setting, character and spooky somebody for your story!

Roll a dice to choose a spooky setting:

1. A haunted mansion.
2. A deep, dark cave.
3. The basement of an abandoned hospital.
4. Lost in a maze!
5. An ancient graveyard.
6. A dimly–lit church.

Choose your fave colour to pick a hero/heroine!

Prince Harry Styles   **Your BF**   **The Prime Minister**

Your mum   **Queen Jacqueline Wilson**   **King Nick Sharratt**

Pick a spooky picture to select a terrifying arch-rival!

ANGEL OF DEATH.

GIANT MAN–EATING, SPIDER!

AGGRESSIVE ALIEN!

DEADLY POISONOUS SNAKE.

Now write your story!
Don't forget to include lots of hair-rising twists and turns!

Spooky Ghoul-oons!

Give your Halloween room a spooky glow!

What are a ghost's favourite rides at the fair?

The scary-go-round and rollerghoster!

You'll need:

- Pack of small green glow sticks
- White balloons
- A black marker

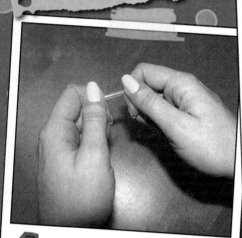

1 Snap your glow sticks so they start to glow.

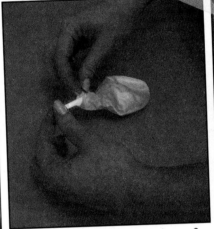

2 Stretch the opening of the balloon slightly and put the glow stick inside. Do this until there are 10–15 inside.

3 Inflate the balloon and then carefully tie it closed. The balloon should now be glowing!

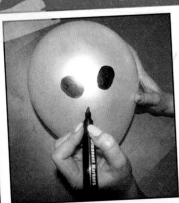

4 Use a black marker to draw a wide–eyed face on the front. Why not try different scary expressions on each balloon?

5

Now just arrange your ghostly balloons around the room and lower the lights. Spooky!

Let's get ARTY!

Show off your artsy ideas with our *Illustrated Mum* design challenges!

I IS FOR ILLUSTRATED

Not only is Marigold covered in intricate tattoos, but she designs them too. What would your tattoo design look like?

Is it mystical like Marigold's sorceress tattoo?

Will it be something you love like a puppy or favourite toy?

It could be a sparkling gemstone!

Get your pens and get busy here —

You could make it like a funny cartoon!

What about a pretty fairy or a shimmering silver moon?

Marigold has a dolphin for Dolphin and a star for Star. Will your design be something that reminds you of a friend or family member?

Or a sinister snake or skull — ooh, creepy.

Will it be girlie with swirly flowers and leaves?

Scrolling Script Writing

Tip! Use a pencil to complete steps 1– 5.

Happy Birthday Marigold

Happy Birthday Marigold

Happy Birthday Marigold

1. Start by lightly sketching out your message. Leave space between each letter for adding your outlines and flourishes.

2. Draw a solid outline round each letter. Star has drawn some curly ends on the letters r, t, h and y. Copy the picture to add them to your message.

3. Next add some pointed flourishes to the ends of other letters. Star has left a couple of letters plain, but you can add the flourishes wherever you like.

4. Now copy the picture to add swirls to the centres of some letters — Star has chosen p, b, d, and g.

Happy Birthday Marigold

6. When you're happy with your design, carefully ink in all the outlines and gently rub off any pencil marks.

5. Pick a trademark shape to finish off the centres of the letters a and o. Star has used stars, but you could choose hearts, flowers or more swirls. Use the shape to dot i or j too.

Happy Birthday Marigold

Happy Birthday Marigold

Now it's time to colour! Why not fill in the letters with glitter glue for extra sparkle?

Design-a-dress!

Dolphin's black velvet dress embroidered with silver moons and stars is the only one she has. Design a lovely new one for her to wear...

What colours will you choose? Dolphin's always in black, but perhaps she'd suit some vivid jewel shades instead.

Dolphin and Marigold go walking by Beech Brook and imagine living in a pretty cottage, so why not try a country design with rabbits and tiny mice?

Or maybe you'll use the colours and motifs of the sea to match her name.

Perhaps you'll draw a dress covered in tattoo designs just like Marigold's.

Dolphin needs some good luck, so your design could include charms like four-leaf clovers, daisy chains, rainbows and horseshoes!

Will you draw a dress for daytime wear or a spectacular party outfit? Dolphin might need some new accessories too.

You could add some glitter or stick on paper, fabric or gems!

You could trim the hems with little jingling bells and add some flowing silk strips to match Dolphin's scarf.

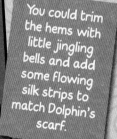

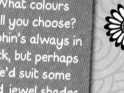

All About Me!

J IS FOR JACKY

Take a peek inside my life!

I hand write all my stories in beautiful Italian notebooks — I'm really not very good at using computers!

This is me on the day I was made a Dame by the Queen!

I lie on my pink velvet chaise lounge and write for an hour or so every morning. Jacob often cuddles up beside me and peers out the window.

All my amazing jewellery comes from a shop called The Great Frog and its sister shop, Curiouser and Curiouser.

I love...

Handbags!

My darling dolls!

Silver jewellery!

Lots and lots of books!

Balle by Noel
The Children Fr
by E
The
Little Women b
A Little Princes
What Ka
Marian
by Cath

The best present I ever received has to be Whisper, my beautiful Victorian-style rocking horse.

My proudest achievement to date is having my very own magazine!

I got the original idea for *Candyfloss* after meeting a kind dad who told me he had his own chip van and his daughter liked curling up in the back and reading my books while he was serving!

Thanks, Dad!

Here's a lovely little group of friends — Famous Monkey, little Robin ted, and my blue velvet Rabbit.

I'm always amazed and touched when fans travel great distances to come and hear me talk.

My adorable pets!

The Victorians!

Did you know?

Jacky has a collection of over 20,000 books!

Best Friends Forever!

Nick Sharratt is one of my closest friends...

We often go on holiday together. Here we are on a trip to a Gothic temple in Stowe!

Here's Nick and me with our mini-people. They were made by a brilliant sculptor called Guy Reid.

Jacqueline Wilson
THE STORY OF Tracy Beaker

The first book we ever worked on together was *The Story of Tracy Beaker!*

Tremendous Terrific Me!

COULD YOU BE The Next JW?

1) The last thing you wrote was...
a) A page in your diary. You write in it every night! ☐
b) An embarrassing moment that you sent into JW Mag! ☐
c) A story that you illustrated with cute little doodles. ☑ 😊

2) Your teacher tells you the class will be reading a book next term. You...
a) Ask if it has any pictures. Hmmmm... ☐
b) Think it sounds bit dull. You'll probably drift off in a daydream... ☐
c) Can't wait till then. You'll read it over the holidays! ☑

3) If you were stuck on a desert island, the object you'd miss most would be...
a) A pen. How would you record your adventures without one? ☐
b) Your art materials. The beach would be so pretty to sketch! ☑
c) Your phone. You'd miss gossiping with your bestie! ☐

4) You're working on a class project at school. You...
a) Do an amazing presentation in front of the class. ☐
b) Write paragraphs and paragraphs about the topic. ☑
c) Paint an amazing picture to stick on the wall! ☐

5) It's your birthday. Your favourite present is...
a) A beautiful notebook. You can't wait to fill it with your best handwriting! ☑
b) It was actually the birthday party with all your friends! ☐
c) A craft set with coloured felt, sequins, ribbons — everything! ☐

6) You've got homework to do. You...
a) Do the fun stuff first — like your art homework. Maths can totally wait. ☑
b) Get a bit distracted and end up phoning your bestie! ☐
c) Get it done as soon as you get back from school. ☐

Your Score!

NOW ADD UP YOUR SCORE!
1a)1b)2c)3 2a)3b)2c)1 3a)1b)3c)2 4a)2b)1c)3 5a)1b)2c)3 6a)3b)2c)1

BETWEEN 6 and 11
WOW — you're spookily like Jacky already! You love reading and writing and you already have loads of pretty notebooks filled up with your story ideas. We really won't be surprised if you're a best-selling author when you're older!

BETWEEN 12 and 14
You're really chatty and bubbly and you ♥ being the centre of attention. You're always telling stories and making your mates laugh about your escapades! Why not try writing down your stories? We bet they would make an amazing book!

BETWEEN 15 and 18
You're a really creative person and are always doodling away or daydreaming about ideas in your head. Writing definitely isn't your favourite thing to do, but we could see you being an illustrator like Nick — you're super-talented!

Where I Live!

> I've lived in Kingston for most of my life — here are my favourite places to visit!

Most people come to Kingston for the shops. I like bookshops most of all! When I was young Kingston used to have many, including a couple of great secondhand bookshops where I spent my pocket money. My favourite Kingston bookshop now is the big branch of Waterstone's in the Bentalls Centre.

I used to live near Richmond Park and went for a walk there every lunchtime when I finished writing. I still walk there as often as possible. It's a huge historic park with fantastic wildlife, including red and fallow deer.

Jackson loves to go to the Fairfield where he has many doggy friends. The Fairfield is a wonderful open green space where schoolchildren play sport, students hang out with friends, and families have picnics.

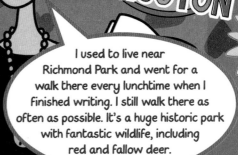

Kingston is officially Kingston-on-Thames and I love taking Jackson for walks along the river Thames. I particularly like the Canbury Park Gardens stretch of the river. I've been walking there since my daughter Emma was a toddler.

I used to love going dancing in Kingston when I was a teenager. There's still a brilliant dance studio with all the original fittings hidden down a side street.

Kingston is famous for its unusual modern sculpture made out of telephone boxes.

Kingston has the very special Rose Theatre. I was so proud when the play of *Hetty Feather* opened there. I went to many performances! It's got a great café too.

K IS FOR KISSES

GIRLS IN LOVE GIFTS!

Make these cute DIY gifts for your besties!

Magda's Friendship Jar!

You'll need:
- A clean, empty jar
- Some coloured paper
- White paper
- Glue
- Pen

1 First, you need to decorate your jar! I cut out some paper hearts and glued them on.

2 Tie a ribbon around the top of your jar — very pretty!

3 Now write some friendship messages on small strips of paper. Think about why you love your BFF — maybe she always laughs at your rubbish jokes or is always there when you want to have a chat?

4 Fold up all the messages and pop them in your jar. You now have the perfect gift for your BFF!

Ellie's Hugs & Kisses Cupcakes!

You'll need: ● VANILLA CUPCAKES ● MINI MARSHMALLOWS ● SCISSORS

Be careful when using scissors!

1 Take some pink mini marshmallows and snip them in half with scissors.

2 Take one of your cupcakes and arrange the marshmallows in an X shape.

3 Take another one of the cupcakes and arrange the marshmallows in a circle shape. Arrange them in a line so they read XOXO — then eat! Yummy!

Nadine's Lolly Card!

You'll need:

YOU'RE SO **COOL**

XOXO

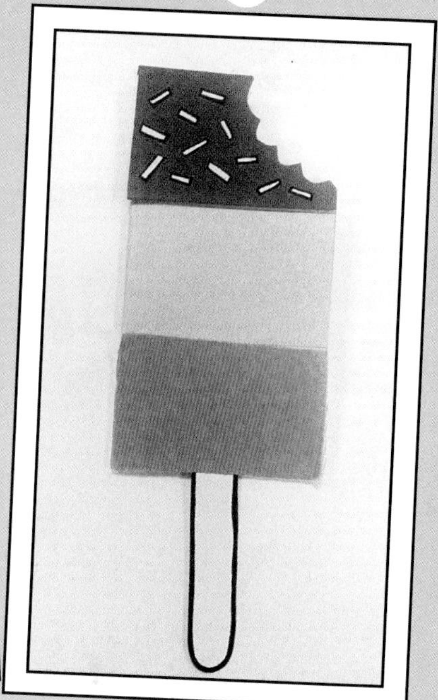

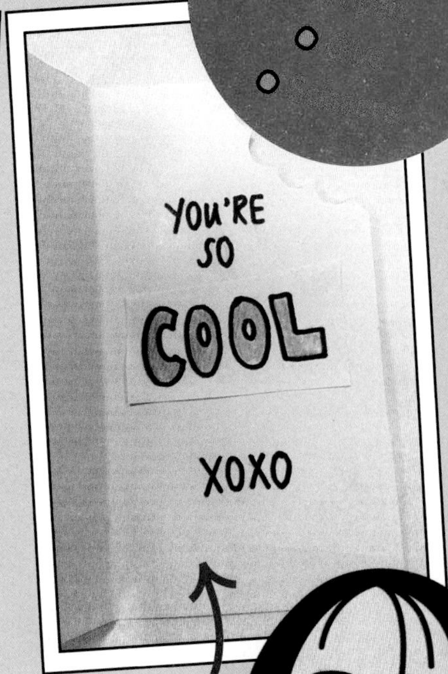

1 Take a piece of card and fold it in half. Divide it into three equal-sized sections. You can use a ruler to get these exactly right. Now, draw a bite mark in the top section and cut out.

2 Now it's time to decorate! I used pink tissue paper on the bottom third and brown foam on the top. Then I cut out some sprinkles from paper and glued them on too!
Draw a lolly stick on paper, cut out and glue to the bottom.

3 Finally, write a cute message on the inside!

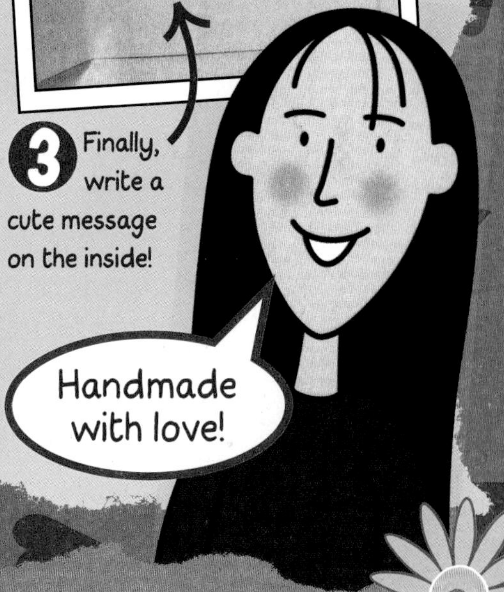

Handmade with love!

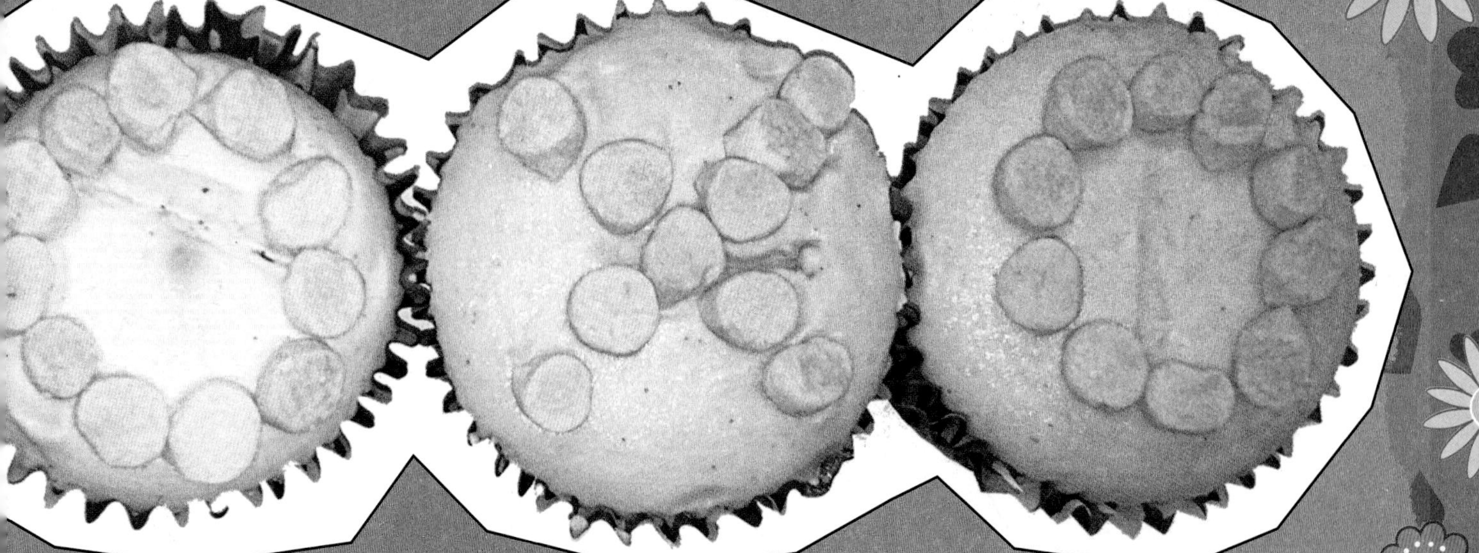

LUCKY CHARM!

Pick the answer that sounds most like you to find out which charm will bring you luck!

1. YOU SEE A BLACK CAT!

A. You cross the road — black cats are bad luck!

B. You stop to say hello!

2. WHICH IS WORSE?

A. Opening an umbrella indoors.

B. Putting shoes on a table.

3. YOU STEP OUTSIDE AND STRAIGHT INTO A PUDDLE!

A. Oops — better pay attention next time!

B. I'm going to have bad luck all day!

4. YOU WOULD RATHER...

A. Walk under a ladder.

B. Walk over a crack on the pavement.

5. YOU SEE A PENNY ON THE GROUND!

A. You pick it up and keep it in your pocket!

B. You pass it on to someone else for luck!

MOSTLY A
FOUR LEAF CLOVER

The chances of finding a four leaf clover are 10,000 to one — so finding one makes you especially lucky! If you don't find one on your first try, why not make one out of card or material? Carry it wherever you go and good luck will follow!

MOSTLY B
LUCKY DICE

When we roll a dice we leave the outcome to chance — which is why rolling a high number is associated with luck! Roll your dice each morning until you reach a number 10 or above for good luck!

MAGIC BLACK CAT!

I'm good luck!

You will always be surrounded by true friends!

LUCK!

Close your eyes and put your finger over the black cat. When you open your eyes, see which duck your eyes are drawn to first to get your lucky fortune!

You are more talented than you know — now is the time to try something new!

Your luck is about to change — a good deed never goes unnoticed!

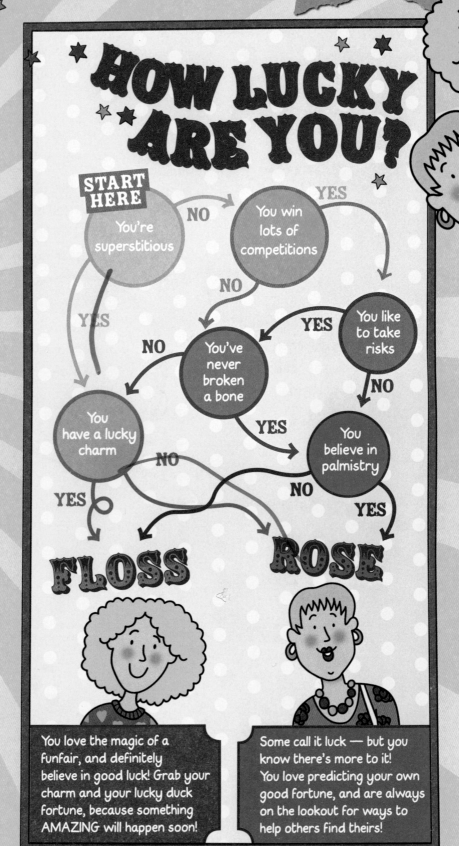

HOW LUCKY ARE YOU?

START HERE

You're superstitious — **NO** → You win lots of competitions — **YES** → You like to take risks

You win lots of competitions — **NO** → You've never broken a bone

You're superstitious — **YES** → You have a lucky charm

You've never broken a bone — **NO** → You have a lucky charm

You've never broken a bone — **YES** → You believe in palmistry

You like to take risks — **NO** → You believe in palmistry

You have a lucky charm — **YES** → FLOSS

You have a lucky charm — **NO** → ROSE

You believe in palmistry — **NO** → FLOSS

You believe in palmistry — **YES** → ROSE

FLOSS

You love the magic of a funfair, and definitely believe in good luck! Grab your charm and your lucky duck fortune, because something AMAZING will happen soon!

ROSE

Some call it luck — but you know there's more to it! You love predicting your own good fortune, and are always on the lookout for ways to help others find theirs!

39

LUCKY DICE NAILS!

YOU'LL HAVE LUCKY FINGERS IN MINUTES WITH THIS CUTE NAIL ART LOOK!

Two thin coats of polish are better than one thick coat!

YOU'LL NEED:

* WHITE NAIL POLISH
* BLACK NAIL POLISH
* A HAIR GRIP

1. Paint your nails white and let dry completely.

2. Pull a hair grip open so that you have one end free. Use this to dot black polish on your nail in a dice design.

3. Continue the design on all your nails, then seal with a clear topcoat to protect them.

Work out which nail is your biggest and do the five dots on it — that way, you won't run out of space!

Why not?

Add a lucky green shamrock to your ring finger? Just use the hair grip to make four dots close together, then add a little tail using the side of the nail polish brush!

Are You Marty Or Melissa?

M IS FOR MARTY & MELISSA

Tick the answer you agree with to find out whether you're glam and girlie Melissa or cool, confident Marty!

The colour pink is...

MY ABSOLUTE FAVOURITE! ✓

ABSOLUTELY DISGUSTING! ☐

Pretty dresses are...

HORRID, HORRID, HORRID! ☐

MY FAVOURITE THING TO WEAR! ✓

Practical jokes are...

SOOO IMMATURE! ☐

REALLY, REALLY FUNNY! ✓

If someone was annoying me, I'd...

THROW SOME EGGS AT THEM! ☐

TUT AND ROLL MY EYES AT THEM. ✓

If I had £10, I'd buy...

LIPBALM, BODY LOTION, ACCESSORIES — AS LONG AS IT'S PRETTY AND PINK! ☐

PENS, SKETCHBOOKS, A MAGAZINE — ANYTHING THAT'S FUN! ✓

Getting ready in the morning takes me...

FIVE MINUTES. AND FOUR OF THOSE ARE SPENT EATING BREAKFAST. ☐

ABOUT HALF AN HOUR — I HAVE TO DO MY HAIR, CHOOSE MY CLOTHES... ✓

Your perfect sleepover would be...

A PAMPER SESSION WHILE GOSSIPING AND WATCHING A ROMANTIC COMEDY FILM! ✓

FULL OF FUN — LOADS OF GAMES AND LOADS OF LOLS! ✓

MOSTLY PINK → Melissa!

Just like Melissa, you're grown-up and girlie and you love anything pink! Having fun with your friends is one of your favourite things to do — and your least favourite? Having your annoying little sister hanging around...

MOSTLY RED → Marty!

You and Marty are like peas in a pod! Having fun is super-important to you, and when anything stops you (read: annoying big sisters) you can't stand it! Oh, and the other thing you can't stand? The colour pink! Ew!

Now turn the page to make Marty and Melissa's t-shirts!

41

THE BEST THING ABOUT MY T-SHIRT...

Make your very own Marty and Melissa tees!

For Melissa's t-shirt you'll need:

- A PINK T-SHIRT
- WHITE FELT
- BLACK FELT
- PINK FELT
- GREEN FELT
- SCISSORS
- PINS
- WATERPROOF FABRIC GLUE

TURN TO PAGE 89 FOR THE PATTERN TEMPLATES!

1 Trace the Melissa t-shirt pattern on to paper, then cut out the individual parts.

2 Pin each pattern piece to the correct colour of felt then cut them out.

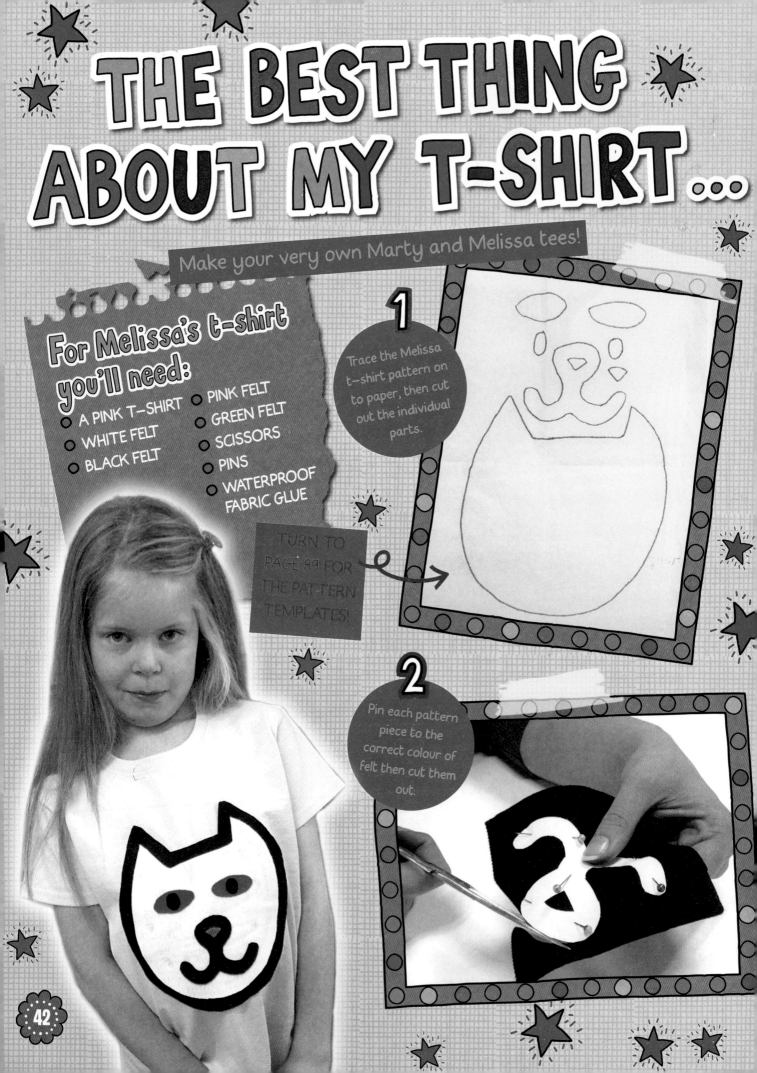

3

Use fabric glue to stick the different parts of the design to your t–shirt — start with the background piece, then start layering them up!

4

Once the glue has dried, start wearing your awesome new tee!

For the Marty tee, just follow the same steps as the Melissa tee. You can either enlarge the template to make it fit the width of your t–shirt, or you can just make a smaller design using the template on *page 89*.

For Marty's t-shirt you'll need:

- A RED T-SHIRT
- BLUE FELT
- YELLOW FELT
- BLACK FELT
- SCISSORS
- PINS
- FABRIC GLUE

Tip!

If you make Marty's design, the yellow and blue felt needs to be at least 45cm by 45cm to fit the width of your t-shirt!

Tip!

If you love sewing, you can stitch on your felt pieces instead!

Pink menaces KEEP OUT!

43

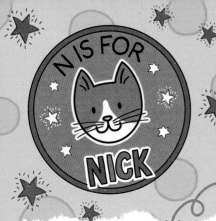

N IS FOR
NICK

WE ♥ NICK

Everything you wanted to know about the amazing illustrator!

NAME: Nick Sharratt

BORN: August 9, 1962, in London

STARSIGN: Leo

JOB: Illustrator and author

ACHIEVEMENTS:

- Illustrated over 250 books!
- Children's Book Award winner
- Past World Book Day official illustrator
- Gold *Blue Peter* badge

HOBBIES: Napping and snoozing. I am a world champion!

FAVE TV SHOW: *The Great British Bake-Off*

SKETCH
BOOK

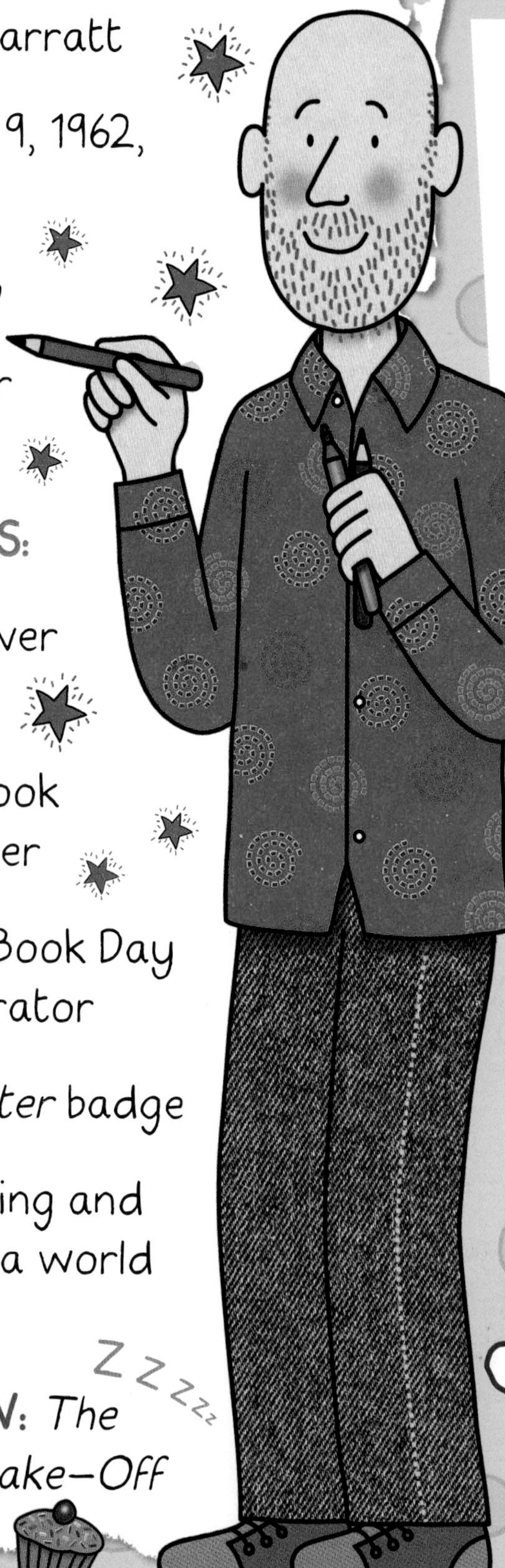

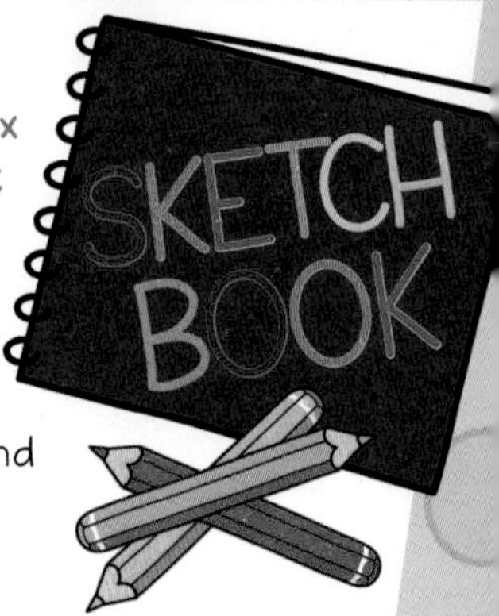

Lulu_Angel
If you could take just six things on holiday, what would you take?
A sun hat for my bald head, a pile of good books, swimming goggles, a sketchpad and pencils, a pair of Crocs and a travel kettle.

Gabriella
What is your favourite fruit?
A crisp, green Granny Smith apple.

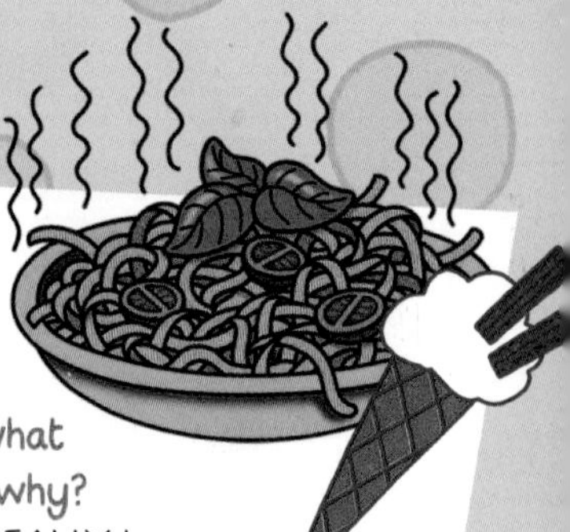

Ella-Rose
If you could invent any ice cream flavour, what would it be and why?
Pesto flavour. I REALLY love pasta with pesto!

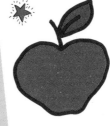

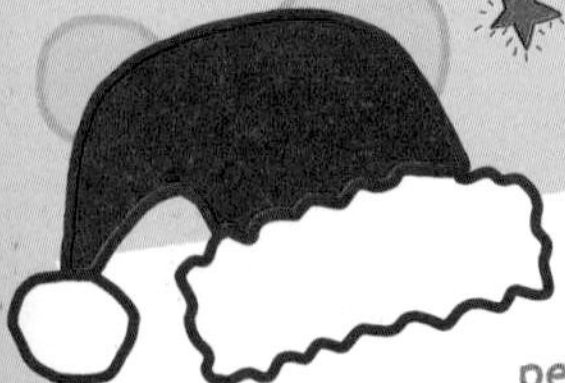

Jade
If there was one person in the whole world you could meet, who would it be and why?
Father Christmas — I could find out how he does it!

SHARRATT!

Nick aged six! Awww!

Abbey
What would you like to be if you weren't an illustrator?
I'd like to be a set designer for films.

Nick's amazing stage set design!

Taurus Temper
If you could be a child for a day, what would you do?
I'd build a den!

Lulu
Of all the drawings you've ever done, which one is your favourite?
A picture of a market square I drew when I was nine — I've still got it!

Imogen
Which is your favourite art gallery and why?
The Guggenheim Museum in Spain. It's the most spectacular building to visit.

Ribh
If you could have painted one artwork that any other artist has painted, which one would you choose and why?
A Sunday on La Grande Jatte by Georges Seurat. It's such a lovely sunny painting.

Head on over to **www.nicksharratt.com** to find out more about Nick and his work!

45

Nick's Picture Prompt!

Can you believe Nick drew this picture when he was only 10?

It's full of tiny details with something new to spot each time you look. Follow the tips and YOU can do it too!

Decide on a theme for your scene. Nick loved drawing busy shopping centres or streets where he could add lots and lots of stuff.

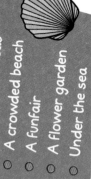

You can make up a scene or draw somewhere you know well. Why not take some photos for inspiration? Here are a few ideas —
- A crowded beach
- A funfair
- A flower garden
- Under the sea

Now it's time to add the finishing details with colour or black and white shading.

Draw in pencil first and, when you're happy with your sketch, start to ink in the outlines.

Nick drew so much he had to tape on more sheets of paper to his picture!

Then just keep adding to fill more and more of the page. It's best to do a little bit every day instead of trying to finish it all in one go.

Start at the bottom left of your page and draw one object or person. Now add a few more things surrounding them. Nick used signs, prams, plants and clocks amongst all the people.

OPAL'S WORLD

O IS FOR OPAL

I was really inspired by the Edwardians for my 100th book, *Opal Plumstead!*

New laws for children were passed by the Edwardians. One law encouraged schools to provide school meals for children — before this, most children turned up to school too hungry to learn — and another stated that children were no longer allowed to be sent out begging or to buy cigarettes!

What would you do if you had to go all day at school without food? Do you think you'd be able to concentrate on learning?

FAIRY GLEN CONFECTIONERY — FAIRY GLEN

Edwardian children had to go to school — but only till they were 12! After that, most children had to find work to help support their families, just like Opal, who goes to work in a sweet factory...

Can you imagine what it would be like to leave school at 12? What would you do if you had to go to work now?

MRS. PANKHURST

Edwardian women weren't allowed to vote, and only men had a say in how the country was run. Many disagreed with this, and set up groups to protest. The Suffragettes were led by Emmeline Pankhurst, who Opal meets in Jacky's book. The Suffragettes did lots of things to try to win the vote for women — they shouted at political meetings, chained themselves to railings, and refused to eat when they were imprisoned, which made them very ill. Eventually, in 1918, women were allowed to vote — but only if they were older than 30! Since 1969, anyone aged 18 and over has the right to vote.

Do you think it was fair that women weren't allowed to vote?

DID YOU KNOW?

Supporters of the Suffragettes wore green, purple and white, which represented hope, dignity and purity!

TURN THE PAGE TO FIND OUT MORE ABOUT THE EDWARDIANS — AND THE VICTORIANS WHO CAME BEFORE THEM!

Jacky's written books set in the Victorian and Edwardian Eras — let's find out more about them!

One will only wear black!

Royalty

Queen Victoria reigned from 1837–1901 — an astonishing 64 years! She was seen as very private, dedicated and respectful, especially when her husband, Albert, died in 1861. After that, Victoria only wore black as a sign of mourning.

King Edward VII became king when Victoria died. He ruled for just nine years, but he made quite an impact! Many people didn't think he'd be a good king because when he was a prince he loved having fun and wasn't thought to be serious enough!

Inventions

Lots of important things were invented in the Victorian and Edwardian eras — in fact, we still use a lot of them today!

PHOTOGRAPHS
POSTBOXES
CHRISTMAS CARDS
SEWING MACHINES
THE TUBE
RADIO

VACUUM CLEANER
AEROPLANE
WINDSHIELD WIPERS
ICE LOLLIES
CELLOPHANE
TEABAGS

Can you imagine what life would be like without these things?

What do you think the most important or useful of these inventions is?

Exceptionally Edwardian!
Fun & Games

We Edwardians knew how to have fun!

The Victorians and Edwardians had lots of fun pastimes that we still enjoy today. Tick all the ones that you've tried.

- ☐ Visit the zoo
- ☐ Go to the theatre
- ☐ See a pantomime
- ☐ Make a scrapbook
- ☐ Play party games
- ☐ Play board games
- ☐ Play table tennis
- ☐ Use a rope to skip
- ☐ Spend the day at the seaside

AQUARIUM ONE CHILD R2587L

Tick all the books you've read, and circle the ones you want to read next!

Brilliant Books

THESE CHILDRENS' BOOKS WERE POPULAR IN VICTORIAN TIMES...

- ☑ *BLACK BEAUTY* by Anna Sewell
- ☐ *ALICE IN WONDERLAND* by Lewis Carroll
- ☑ *TOM BROWN'S SCHOOL DAYS* by Thomas Hughes
- ☑ *LITTLE WOMEN* by Louisa May Alcott
- ☑ *WHAT KATY DID* by Susan Coolidge

Jacky has written her own version of this, called *Katy*!

... AND THESE ONES IN EDWARDIAN TIMES:

- ☑ *FIVE CHILDREN AND IT* by E. Nesbit
- ☑ *PETER PAN* by J. M. Barrie
- ☑ *THE TALE OF PETER RABBIT* by Beatrix Potter
- ☐ *THE WIND IN THE WILLOWS* by Kenneth Graeme
- ☑ *THE RAILWAY CHILDREN* by E. Nesbit
- ☑ *THE SECRET GARDEN* by Frances Hodgson Burnett

I ♥ Animals!

I badly wanted a dog when I was growing up, but we lived in a council flat and pets just weren't allowed. But now I've now got three little fur-babies to call my own! Jacob and Lily are my lovely pet cats and Jackson the dog is the newest addition to our furry family!

I met all three at Battersea Dogs & Cats Home, where I've worked as an ambassador since 2012. I love the fact that in spite of their unfortunate starts in life, nearly all Battersea dogs and cats become wonderful, loving pets!

I found Jacob first, when he was a very tiny, timid little kitten. He hid under my bed a lot. I used to sit and quietly chat to him so he'd get used to the sound of my voice.

LOVE AT FIRST SIGHT...

Jackson was a tiny puppy when I first saw him. He'd been left tied up to some railings, but in spite of this was immensely friendly and trusting and jumped on my lap.

Jacob and Lily keep me company when I write!

I discovered Lily one Christmas. She'd been very ill in the Battersea hospital — but when I lifted her up she settled happily and kneaded my fur coat, mistaking me for her mother.

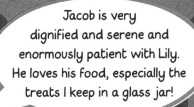

Lily is a mischievous little girl cat who cuddles close and sings herself to sleep. She thinks Jacob is a great big snuggly toy and always tries to curl up with him!

Jacob is very dignified and serene and enormously patient with Lily. He loves his food, especially the treats I keep in a glass jar!

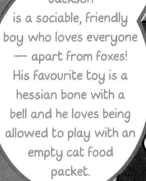

Jackson is a sociable, friendly boy who loves everyone — apart from foxes! His favourite toy is a hessian bone with a bell and he loves being allowed to play with an empty cat food packet.

Who's The Boss?

Jacob gains the most respect, but Lily frequently manages to get her own way! Jackson is the noisiest and is very determined. I would say they take it in turns to be the boss!

Naughtiest Pet?

Jackson is by far the most mischievous...

● He has occasionally seized the post and started chewing it to shreds if over-excited.

● He has a mind of his own, and will sit down and protest if he realises we're leaving the park.

● He dashes up and down the stairs whenever we try to put his harness on, even though he loves going for walks. He just likes playing chase!

I ♥ My Pet!

Write about your favourite pet or animal here —

NAME: .... Sky Tiger

TYPE OF ANIMAL: .... cat

NAUGHTY OR NICE? .... Nice

THREE THINGS THEY LIKE

1. .... Sleep
2. .... Playing
3. .... Cuddle

Stick a photo or drawing of your pet here!

Make these funny bunny biscuits — I'll show you how!

MAKE BURROWING BUNNIES!

You'll need:

- Your favourite cookie dough mix
- Pink and white icing
- Mini marshmallows
- Baking paper to line your tray
- Sprinkles to decorate

We used pink and white icing, but why not come up with your own colour combinations?!

1. Roll out the dough to around ½cm thick, cut out some circles and place them on to a lined baking tray.

2. Make feet from dough scraps. Roll a piece into a little ball and flatten into an oval. You'll need two for each cookie.

Tip! Roll your dough between two pieces of baking paper. This will stop it sticking to the rolling pin or table top!

3. Bake all the shapes in the oven for around 10—12 minutes until a light golden brown, following your recipe's instructions. Remove from the oven and leave on the tray to cool.

Ask an adult for help when using the oven!

You could add some jelly beans to the top for bunny ears!

4. Now ice the big circles pink and the smaller ones white. Place two of the white ovals on top of the pink ones to make your bunny bottoms and feet!

5. Add a mini marshmallow for a fluffy bunny tail, and use cake sprinkles to make the detail on the feet. A little icing will help them stick. All done — now it's time to eat them! Deeelicious!

52

Imagine If...

YOU were Elsie Kettle!

Q IS FOR QUEENIE

The Queen's Coronation would be the talk of the country! People everywhere would be making plans to travel to London for the big day.

You'd live in a cosy basement flat, just you and Nan!

You'd meet the Queen herself! What would you say to her?

....

....

....

Nurse Gabriel would take such good care of you. She'd surprise you with little treats and presents.

You'd have to spend a l-o-o-o-n-g time in hospital, poor you. But just think of all the cuddles you could have with Queenie!

Mum would visit and bring little gifts to cheer you up. Make a list of all the things you might like if you were poorly and stuck in bed:

....

....

....

Friend or Foe?

Tick the children on the ward you'd most like to be friends with!

☐ **Martin**
He likes comics and jokes!

☑ **Michael**
He's a happy, loving little boy.

☑ **Gillian**
She's bold, brave and a loyal friend.

☑ **Angus**
Is super-clever and kind.

☐ **Rita**
She's a girlie-girl who likes pretty things.

53

PURR-FECT PALS!

Copy Queenie!

When Elsie Kettle is separated from her beloved nan, she finds a new friend in Queenie, a fluffy white cat.

Nick's Tip!

Grab your pencil and draw Queenie! Use the squares to help you sketch — just copy what you see in each one.

Now try drawing Queenie on plain paper. Why not glue on some ribbon as a pretty collar or add some press—on jewels?!

NO SEW CAT BED!

Your pet will love lounging on this plumptious cushion!

1. Get *1 metre* of fleece fabric and fold it in half short edge to short edge. Cut into two equal pieces and place one piece on top of the other.

Measure in 12cm from all four edges and draw lines with chalk. It should look like this.

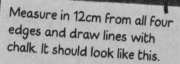
Place rulers here for a guide!

2. Snip off the four corner sections. Next cut fringes approx. 2cm wide up to the lines along each edge. You don't have to be too exact.

8. Start to securely knot the fringes together to join one layer of fabric to the other. When you've done three sides pop an old pillow between the two layers. Finish knotting the last side and that's it done!

Fit for a Queenie!

What a Cat-astrophe!

Cats are curious creatures, and always getting up to mischief. Why not try writing about a nosy or naughty cat?

Will your cat character be a tiny kitten that's full of beans?

Will they be a precious pampered puss or a moggy from the streets?

Maybe you could base your story on your own pet kitty!

Will curiosity get them into trouble or help them solve a tricky problem? You decide!

Maybe your kitty will have a super special power, or an unusual friend to help them out!

Will you write about me?

Paws for Thought!

Have fun coming up with some cat-related words to use in your story!

Pawsome = Awesome	Meow = Now
Pawsitive = Positive	Furry = Very
Furever = Forever	Purrfect = Perfect
Cat-titude = Attitude	Feline = Feeling

Write your own here!

R IS FOR RED FACES

Rate these hilarious howlers!

Red Face Ratings

So shameful! ★★★
No way! ★★★★
Major blush! ★★★★★

And The Winner Is...

When I was in Year Six we had an important awards assembly and I was chatting with my friend at the back. Suddenly, I heard what I thought was my name and bounded up to the front, beaming happily, with my hand outstretched for the certificate... only to find that it was another girl's name that had been called. I meekly retreated to my seat, my cheeks flaming!

Yolanda, Enfield

Red Face Rating — Mb

Monday Mix-up

It was Monday morning and I was waiting outside my registration class, wondering why there was no one else around. Ten minutes passed and STILL nobody showed up. I sneaked a peek inside the classroom — empty. Confused, I asked a passing teacher where my class was and she reminded me that I was supposed to be in assembly! I charged down the corridor, threw open the hall door and saw my whole class staring back at me! Whoops!

Belen, London

Red Face Rating —

Pool Palaver!

I was on holiday in Greece and having the time of my life playing in the pool. When I dived into the deep end my goggles came loose and water got in my eyes. I started to panic, flapping my arms around and feeling for the pool wall when I grabbed something else — someone's foot! Mega cringe!

Iris, Oxford

Red Face Rating — Mw

Blushes EVER!

Shopping FAIL!

I was going shopping one night with my mum and dad and chose some comfy ballet pumps to wear. We were walking down the snack aisle when I randomly decided to start skipping. All of a sudden, my shoe went flying off, bouncing off the ceiling and landing on the highest shelf! My dad searched through loads and loads of packets of crisps, but couldn't find it anywhere. In the end we had to call one of the staff who brought a ladder to get my shoe back!

Katie, Northallerton

Red Face Rating —

School Shame!

It was the end—of—term assembly and our class had been chosen to sing in front of the whole school — and our parents! I was nervously trying to remember the words to the song when I heard my classmates laughing hysterically. Looking out over the crowd, I spotted a group of people doing a Mexican wave! I started giggling, too — until I realised it was MY FAMILY! Oh, the embarrassment...

Ribh, Aberdeen

Red Face Rating —

Wildlife Woe!

I was on a school trip in the country when one of my classmates shouted that they had found a frog on the riverbank! I dashed across the bridge and clambered down the muddy embankment, desperate to take a look. I guess I really should've paid more attention to where I was going... I slipped and fell in the river! Everyone was laughing as I pulled myself out of the water!

Esme, Norwich

Red Face Rating —

Cringe Confession!

I NEVER get embarrassed! Well, maybe sometimes... I mean, it was pretty cringing when Garnet mucked up our audition for The Twins at St Clare's! Oh, and maybe cutting my hair so short wasn't such a great idea — Blob and the gang called me Baldie and I got mistaken for a boy so many times!

Ruby, *Double Act*

Red Face Rating —

Suffered the worst cringe EVER? Turn over to find out how to beat those blushes!

57

Beat Those Blushes!

How to get over your cringes — the Ruby way!

FIRST THINGS FIRST...
You're not alone, OK? Everyone (even the Queen!) has embarrassed one's self at some time or another. Unfortunately, this is your turn in the spotlight, but don't worry — it will pass and you will be completely fine. I promise!

See more cringes in every issue of JW Mag!

MAKE YOUR FAIL FUNNY!
Your epic embarrassing moment has passed and you're left wishing the ground would swallow you up. Did anyone see? Nope? Then push the incident to the back of your mind and carry on with your day. Yes? Try a little laugh or a roll of the eyes and dust yourself down. People are more likely to laugh along with you, rather than AT you.

LOL IT OFF!
Are your friends/foes/family/classmates giving you stick for your unfortunate, erm, mishap? Forget it! Just laugh it off (even if you don't find it funny) and change the subject. I bet they'll soon get bored of talking about the same old thing (yawn!). In fact, they'll have moved on to something else before you know it.

I'm not sure Garnet found it easy to laugh THIS off...

PUT IT IN PERSPECTIVE!
OK, so you've just experienced the most cringe—worthy moment EVER but, let's face it, things could definitely be worse. Don't believe me? Make a list of all the positive things that are going on in your life right now. It might be a sleepover you've got to look forward to, a friendly smile someone gave you or a new top you bought. Whatever it is, no matter if it's big or small, jot it down! You've got a lot to be thankful for, right?

DON'T FORGET TO SMILE!
Still feeling glum? Then fake it! You can make yourself feel instantly better by thinking happy thoughts and making an effort to smile. The more you enjoy yourself, the easier it will be to forget that dratted cringe!

58

Nick's Doodle & Design!

Let your imagination run free! Design amazing t—shirts for the JW gang with me!

S IS FOR SKETCH

Jodie

Jodie has her own unique style! Have fun creating a totally over—the—top tee for her!

Daisy

Daisy is a real girlie girl! You could use glitter glue to add sparkle to your design!

Dolphin

Let's give Dolphin a vibrant, cheery t—shirt — the exact opposite of her usual black dress!

Tina

Pretty butterflies would make a great design for Tina! Colourful AND cute!

Nick

Now design a shirt for me! I like bright, bold colours and funky patterns.

Jacky

And a top for me, please! I like black and silver prints, and intricate designs!

59

MY DREAMHOUSE SCRAPBOOK!

Follow my simple speedy sketches to create a glamorous home for ME!

Chaise Longue

1.   2.   3.

The perfect place to lie back and relax with a box of Very Posh Chocs! Yum yum!

Ornate Mirror

1.

2.   3.

We girls have to look our very best...

Retro Telephone

WELL DONE TRACY!

THE GREATEST PERFORMANCE EVER!

Big—shot film directors will be calling day and night, begging for the Tremendously Talented Tracy Beaker to appear in their latest blockbuster!

1.   2.

3.

Crystal Chandelier

Just like the one in my mum's swanky pad!

1.
2.
3.

Luxury Bed

STRICTLY PRIVATE

My bedroom must be especially glamorous, of course! No enemies allowed — that means YOU, Justine–Dull–As–Dishwater–Littlewood!

1.
2.
3.

Exotic Flowers

1.
2.
3.

Because I'm worth it!

TURN OVER FOR MORE ME!

61

Could you be an Editor Extraordinaire, correcting the manuscripts of top authors like me?

...Be an Editor!

Take my test to see if you can spot the 10 deliberate mistakes in this part of my story —

Once upon a time there was a little girl called Tracey Beaker. That sounds a bit stupid, like the start of a soppy fairy story. I cant stand fairy stories. They're all the same. If your very good and very beautiful with long golden curls then, after sweeping up a few cinders or having a long kip in a cobwebby place, this prince comes along and you love happily ever after.

Which is fine if you happen to be a goodie-goodie and look gorgeous. But if you're bad and ugly then you've got no chance whatsoever You get given a silly name like Rumpelstiltskin and nobody invites you to their party and no one's ever greatful when you do them a whopping great favour. So of course you get a bit cheesed of with this sort of treatment. You stamp your hands in a rage and fall right through the floorboards or you scream yourself into a frenzy and you get locked up in a towel and they throw away the key. i've done a bit of stamping and screaming in my time.

...Make an excuse!

My random excuse generator can help you out of any sticky situation! Just roll a dice...

Roll once and pick one thing from these lists —

ODDS
A BALD CAT
MY BROTHER
AN ALIEN
THE BUS DRIVER

EVENS
AN ELEPHANT
TWO ODD SHOES
A GHOST
MY GRANNY

Roll the dice twice and add your scores to pick one from this section —

2. CHEWED
3. HID
4. THREW AWAY
5. TOASTED
6. STOLE
7. SQUASHED
8. JUMPED ON
9. UNRAVELED
10. SPLASHED
11. SHREDDED
12. CONFISCATED

Roll once then choose from one of these lists —

ODDS
MY LUNCH
THE DOOR KEYS
MY HOMEWORK
THE SHOWER

EVENS
THE SCHOOL BUS
ALL MY CLOTHES
MY SCHOOL BAG
MY SECRET DIARY

A bald cat unraveled all my clothes!

BEAKER BONUS!
Turn to **page 85** to play my Do or Discuss game!

Turn to **page 85** to play my Do or Discuss game!

ANSWERS:
1. Line 1, 'Tracy' is spelt with an e. 2. Line 2, 'cant' instead of 'can't'. 3. Line 3, 'your' instead of 'you're'. 4. Line 5, spelling mistake 'love' instead of 'live'. 5. Line 7, full-stop missing after 'whatsoever'. 6. Line 9, 'greatful' instead of 'grateful'. 7. Line 10, 'cheesed of' instead of 'cheesed off'. 8. Line 10, 'stamp your hands' instead of 'feet'. 9. Line 12, 'towel' instead of 'tower'. 10. Line 13, missing capital on 'I've'.

Am I telling Whopping Great Fibs or being Oh-So-Honest? You decide!

Tracy's TRUE or FALSE!

1 Justine-Can't-Keep-Her-Hands-To-Herself-Littlewood broke my Mickey Mouse alarm clock

◯ Totally Truthful ☐
☽ Beaker Bluff ☑

2 I once went out in the garden Completely and Utterly NAKED!

◯ Totally Truthful ☑
☽ Beaker Bluff ☐

3 Miss Simpkins gave me the part of the Ghost of Christmas Present in our school's play of *A Christmas Carol*.

◯ Totally Truthful ☐ ☽ Beaker Bluff ☑

HURRAY!

THE GREATEST PERFORMANCE EVER!

WELL DONE TRACY!

MAGNIFICENT!

A TRUE STAR IS BORN!

4 The Dumping Ground's pet rabbit is called Cabbage. I'd much prefer a big Rottweiler to scare away my enemies! (That means YOU, Justine-Better-Watch-Out-Littlewood!)

◯ Totally Truthful ☐ ☽ Beaker Bluff ☐

5 My dream meal is a strawberry milkshake, Big Mac and fries from McDonald's — yum yum!

◯ Totally Truthful ☐
☽ Beaker Bluff ☐

6 My birthday is on December 8. I expect my mum will shower me with Incredibly Expensive and Tasteful presents!

◯ Totally Truthful ☐
☽ Beaker Bluff ☐

ANSWERS:
1. Beaker Bluff — Tracy broke Justine's Mickey Mouse Clock. 2. Totally Truthful! 3. Beaker Bluff — Tracy played Ebenezer Scrooge. 4. Beaker Bluff — The rabbit is called Lettuce. 5. Totally Truthful! 6. Beaker Bluff — Tracy's birthday is May 8.

64

Make A Butterfly Feeder!

You'll need:

- **A ROUND TRAY** (use an old foil serving platter or pizza packaging)
- **STICKY TACK**
- **A PENCIL**
- **STRING** (cut this into three lengths, each about 50cm long)
- **BEADS**
- **SCISSORS**
- **FRUIT**

1

Use the pencil to push three holes through the edge of the tray at equal points — they should be in a triangle shape. Place the sticky tack underneath the tray as you do this to protect the work surface!

2

Attach a bead to each length of your string like this.

3

Push the other end of your string through the hole so that the bead is *under* the tray. Add some more beads to the top for decoration! Repeat for the other lengths of string.

4

Gather the strings and tie them together in a knot, then place a larger bead on top of the knot and tie another knot to secure it in place. Use the string tails to tie your feeder to a hook, post or branch outdoors.

5

On a sunny day, place lots of fruit on your feeder and wait for the butterflies to flock to it!

DID YOU KNOW?

Butterflies love fruit that has started to spoil!

The Butterfly Club!

Most butterflies feed on the nectar from flowers, though there are a couple of types that like to munch on other insects or even blood — ew!

Butterflies are cold-blooded and use the heat from the sun to warm up their bodies so they're able to fly. That's why you often see butterflies doing a spot of sunbathing!

North American Monarch butterflies migrate up to 3,000 miles so that they can stay in warmer places like Mexico for the winter!

The smallest butterfly in the world has a wingspan of just over 1cm, while the largest has a wingspan of 30cm!

There are over 175,000 species of butterflies in the world — most of them live in tropical places!

To turn from a caterpillar into a winged adult, each butterfly goes through a process called metamorphosis. This has four stages: egg, caterpillar, pupa and adult.

Butterfly wings are made up of lots of tiny little coloured scales, which give the creatures their pretty patterns!

Peacock butterflies are found across Europe, Russia and Asia — a distance of over 10,000 miles!

Butterflies have their taste receptors on their feet! Imagine tasting the ground everywhere you walked — no wonder they fly!

smallest

largest

SOMETHING SPECIAL!

Colour in the butterflies on the page!

Can you sort the names of these species of butterflies into the grid to reveal something very dear to Tina?

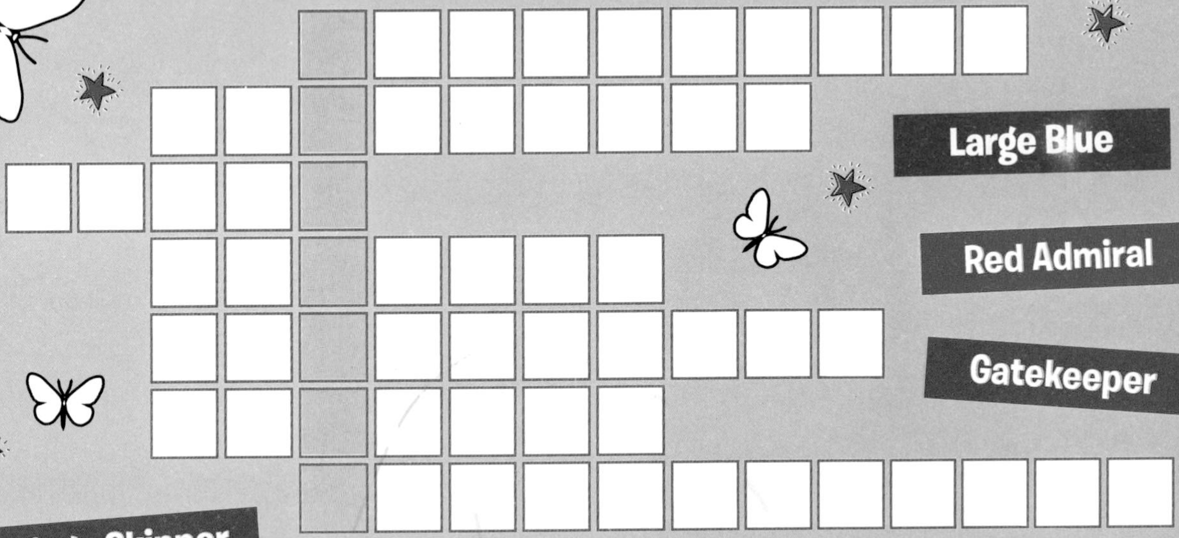

Large Blue

Red Admiral

Gatekeeper

Dingy Skipper

Comma

Monarch

Peacock

- - - - - - - - - - -

WING IT!

Grab your best pens and colour in these butterflies your way!

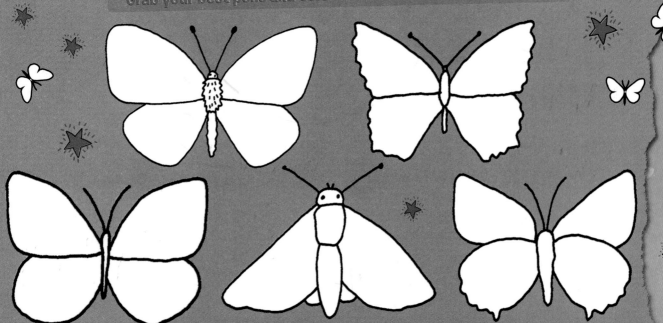

V IS FOR

VICTORIAN

I can help you divine a story...

VICTORIAN

The Victorians loved using parlour games to help them tell the future. Use their divination tricks to write your own Victorian story — your best friend can play too!

Apple Magic!

An ordinary apple was the most mystical of fortune telling tools for Victorian ladies! Why not use one to create a character for your story? Get your best friend to take part, too!

The Name Game

Take an apple and carefully peel it one long strip. Throw the peel over your left shoulder or into a bowl of water and see what letter it forms. Use your letter to find your character's name from this list —

A = Agnes Bottomly

B = Betsy Button   **C** = Cora Goodwin   **D** = Doris Bloom   **E** = Ethel Lovat

F = Florence Richmond   **G** = Gwendolyn Pearce   **H** = Harriet Knight

I = Iris Pegsworth   **J** = Jewel Larkin   **K** = Kitty Dove

L = Louisa Lemon   **M** = Millicent Jones   **N** = Nettie Spencer

O = Olivia Pratt   **P** = Pearl Smedley   **Q** = Queenie Cranwel

R = Rose Taylor   **S** = Sylvia Sparrow   **T** = Tabitha Webb

U = Ursula Trinkett   **V** = Violet Cotton   **W** = Winnifred Kettle

X = Xenia Ebelthrift   **Y** = Yvette Parris   **Z** = Zella Green

My Character's Name:

Rosa taylor

Get your best friend to peel an apple and find her character's name, too!

My BF's Character's Name:

ethel lovat

PARLOUR PARTY!

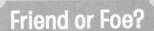

Personality Pips!

Now, both cut your apples open and count out how many apple pips you have. Match these up to a personality trait below.

1. Feisty with a sharp tongue that gets her in trouble!

2. Kind and caring, especially to animals.

3. Too honest — she always tells the truth, even when she shouldn't.

4. Always up for an adventure!

5. Shy, but brilliant!

6. A day-dreamer with an overactive imagination.

7. Spiteful and jealous. Oh-oh!

8. Ambitious and determined to change her life for the better.

9. Secretive with a mysterious past.

Friend or Foe?

How will your two characters get along? Here's how to find out...

What to do

Take an apple pip and place it in a bowl of water with your friend's apple pip, then watch what happens next...

★ If both pips float, your characters will be best friends! Yay!

☆ If they both sink, they'll be worst enemies.

★ If one sinks and one floats, your characters will have a falling out — eek!

Turn to page 93 and use the Fortune Finder to reveal a plot point for your dramatic tale!

Scry a Setting!

Use the map on   to find a suitable setting for your story.

What to do

Thread a bead onto the end of a piece of ribbon and tie it off. Hover your ribbon over the map on page 91 and close your eyes, repeating your character's name in your head. Let the bead drop down and wherever it lands will reveal the perfect setting for your story!

Decisions, decisions...

TANGLEFIELD'S CIRCU

Turn to page 70 to draw your character!

MIRROR, MIRROR!

What would your characters see if they looked in the mirror? Draw their reflections below.

Freaky Fact!

Victorians believed that if you gazed into a mirror at midnight on Halloween, you'd see more than your reflection gazing back — perhaps the spirit of a dead relative, or the face of your future husband, peeking over your left shoulder! Spooky!

My Top 10 Writing Tips!

W IS FOR WRITING

Want to be an author like Jacky? Just follow her top ten tips!

1. Read as many books as possible to see how other writers tell their stories.

2. *I write in my journal every day!*

Keep a diary to develop a regular writing habit.

3. Think very carefully about your characters until you feel you know exactly what they look like and what they'll do and say.

4. Have an interesting and original beginning to your story.

5. Introduce some conflict, so that your characters have to struggle.

6. Use fresh, interesting vocabulary.

7. Don't let your story fade away when you get tired.

8. Try to tie up all the loose ends of your plot.

Use a thesaurus to find Tremendous and Impressive new words!

9. Don't hurry the ending, even if you're desperate to finish it.

10. Read your story through carefully when it's complete and try to make little improvements.

The tips I'm going to follow to improve my writing are...

....

....

....

KEEP READING,

Take our reading and writing challenges!

How would you have written our stories?

Use the first sentences from our books...

...to start a totally new tale.

You can write whatever you like!

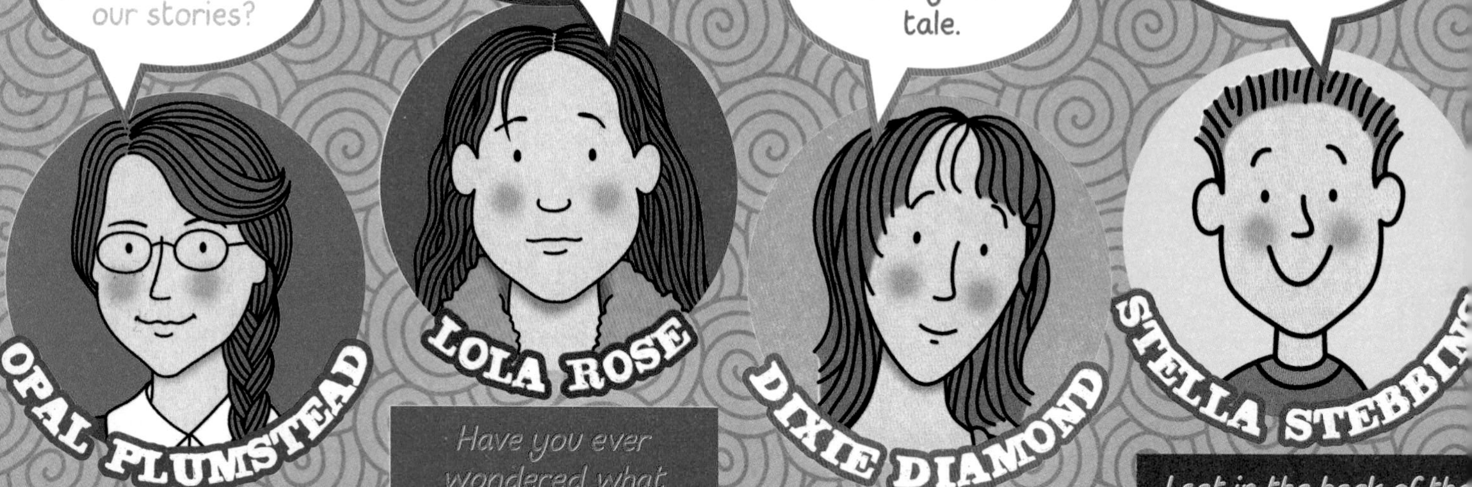

OPAL PLUMSTEAD

'Do you believe in ghosts?' Olivia asked.

LOLA ROSE

Have you ever wondered what you'd do if you won the lottery?

DIXIE DIAMOND

'I've got a surprise for you girls,' said Mum. 'We're moving.'

STELLA STEBBINS

I sat in the back of the car in my new t-shirt and my stiff new jeans and my pristine trainers and groaned.

The Rainbow of Writing

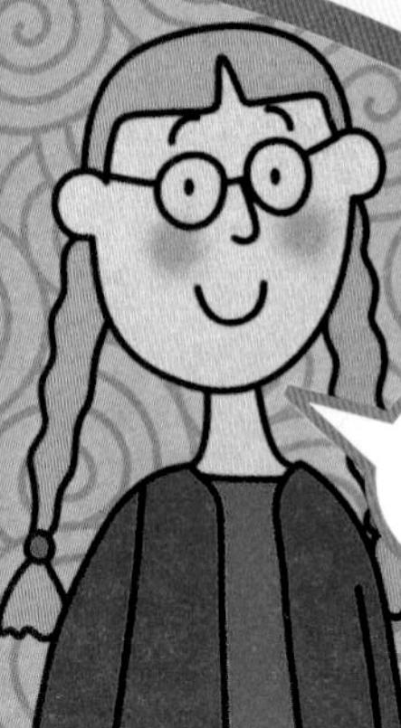

DESCRIBE YOUR FEELINGS THROUGH COLOUR!

RED: The red dress made me feel daring and confident. I was brave and could take on any of those bullies!

ORANGE:

YELLOW:

GREEN:

BLUE: The azure blue pool was calm and serene. Swimming made me relax.

INDIGO:

VIOLET:

I've given you two examples to get started.

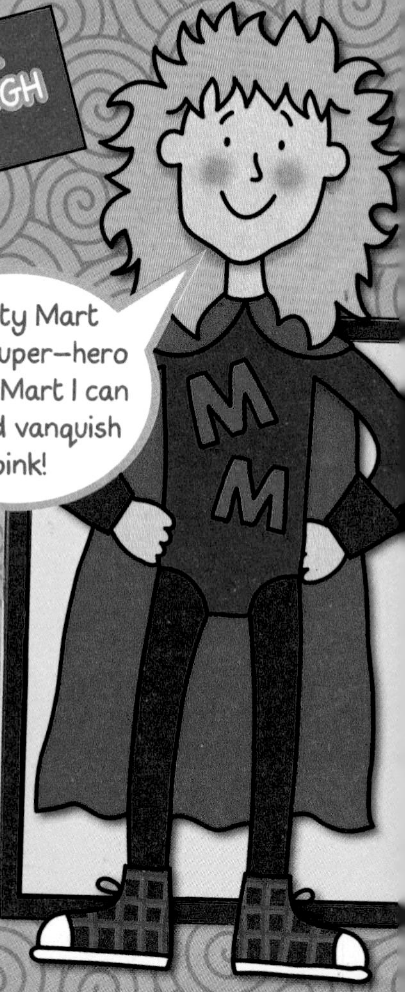

Mighty Mart is the super-hero me! As Mart I can fly and vanquish pink!

KEEP WRITING!

IN THE NEWS!

My story really got started with a newspaper headline!

DUSTBIN BABY!

College student Frankie Smith, 17, found a surprise waiting for him when he did his evening shift at The Pizza Place in the High Street yesterday. He heard a high-pitched wailing coming from the refuse bins at the back of the popular restaurant.

'I thought it was a cat,' said Frankie. 'I got the shock of my life when I took the dustbin lid off and saw the baby.'

The Daily News
DUSTBIN BABY!

Look for a newspaper headline that grabs your attention. Now write your own story based on the headline you choose.

Ever wondered what happens to JW characters after the end of the story?

Choose your fave book and write the next chapter of their tale.

WHAT HAPPENS NEXT?

- Think carefully about how the book ended and what you'd like to happen next.
- Perhaps a tragedy is turned into a triumph, or maybe the character finds fame and fortune!
- What about pairing up characters that appeared in different books?

It's all up to you, so pick up a pen and get started!

SUPER STORY

Who would you be if you were a super-hero? Write your super-hero story, describing your outfit and powers. How would you save the world? Who would be your nemesis?

SUPER GIRLY GIRL

Mortal enemy!

MY 2016 READING GOAL!

In 2016 I'm going to read one book

- ☐ EVERY WEEK
- ☐ EVERY TWO WEEKS
- ☐ EVERY MONTH

Signed: ....

X Factor Star?

YES

You wish you lived in another era...

NO

YES

You'd worry if you got a B in a test.

NO

YES

You exaggerate to make things funnier.

YES

You've got your own alter-ego.

YES

YES

Getting in trouble? No thanks!

NO

You don't like to boast about your talents.

NO

NO

You'd moan if you had to wear a dress.

YES

YES

YES

YES

NO

You Heart Garnet!

She's sweet, shy and really, really clever, just like you! You also like the fact that Garnet doesn't have to be loud and obnoxious to get noticed — her talent is spotted on its own merit. It's great that you're so modest, but sometimes it's really nice to share your stuff with others, too.

You Heart Hetty!

You love history and that's one of the reasons you love this girl so much. But you also admire her fiery nature, and the fact that she'll stick up for herself even when she is a lowly servant — she won't put up with any nonsense from anyone!

You Heart Marty!

You're a huge fan of Marty! You admire her tomboy nature and the fact that there's NO WAY she's going to wear a dress because she's a girl. Pink can take a hike too. You're also really creative — your comic book all about YOU will definitely make you famous one day!

True or False?

How much do you know about Jacky's childhood?

1 Jacky is an only child. T ☑ F ☑

2 She wrote her first novel when she was 10 years old. T ☑ F ☑

3 Her favourite food as a child was pie and mash! T ☑ F ☑

4 She was born in Bath. T ☑ F ☑

5 Her favourite subject in school was Art. T ☑ F ☑

6 Jacky had a cat called Herby when she was small! T ☑ F ☑

7 Her nickname was Jacky Daydream. T ☑ F ☑

8 Jacky wanted to be a teacher when she was younger. T ☑ F ☑

9 Her favourite toy was a dog called Vip! T ☑ F ☑

10 She had lots of pets when she was younger, just like she does now! T ☑ F ☑

Grade your guesses!
How many did you get right?

5 or more:
Wow — your answers are spot on! You'll be a JW expert in no time!

Less than 5:
You've still got lots to learn. But don't worry, this annual is packed full of JW facts!

Y IS FOR YOUNG

Jacky's Picture Album

Jacky shares her photo memories!

Photos are such a great way to capture memories, and are great fun to look back on when you're older! Take a look at these pictures of me growing up!

Here I am as a baby!

This is me and my mum, Biddy, and my dad, Harris!

This is me with some of my favourite dolls

English was one of my favourite subjects at school when I was little!

Here I am laughing with my old school friend, Chris!

Mr Townsend was my favourite teacher at school!

Now make your own timeline!

Make Your Own Photo Bunting!

Make your photos into a hanging timeline!

You'll need:

- Your fave photos
- A4 white card
- Glue
- Scissors
- Pegs
- Ribbon or string

Ask your mum or dad for photos that you've never seen before — it's a great opportunity to find out more about your childhood!

1. Once you've chosen your photos, follow the instructions for trimming them and cutting some card frames.

2. Glue around the edges on the back of your photo and carefully press down onto the card. Remember to leave enough space around your photo to make it look like an old Polaroid!

3. Line up your photos from oldest to newest and secure on your ribbon or string with pegs. Now it's ready to hang!

- Trace this template and cut a pattern from paper.
- Use the pattern to cut some pieces of card to this size.
- Trim your photos to this size.

Why not paint the pegs your favourite colour?

You can write about your photo here.

Z IS FOR ZODIAC

MARIGOLD'S Zodiac Storyteller!

Play my game to create a story that's written in the stars!

What to do:

- Turn to page 87 to find your Zodiac Story Cards. Cut them out and pop them in a bag.
- Roll a dice to make selections from sections A, B and C — story setting, character and story twist.
- Each time you play, pick out three random cards.
- Follow the cards to add extra plot twists to your story.
- Pick one card from the three you've chosen to reveal personality traits for your character.

Play again and again to get different outcomes!

A. Your story setting is...

1. Oops! You're locked in a shopping mall at night.

2. A theme park full of exciting rides and rollercoasters.

3. A really boring and tiresome school lesson.

4. You're staying in a super—creepy old hotel.

5. You have to work as a maid in a posh house.

6. An old—fashioned store selling all sorts of curious goods.

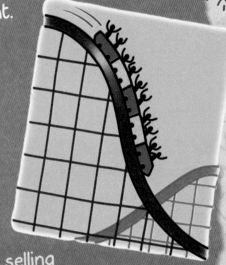

B. Your character is...

1. A Victorian orphan.
2. Tracy Beaker's long-lost twin.
3. A cheeky ten-year-old boy.
4. A spoiled rich girl.
5. A very shy and timid person.
6. A super-brainy know-it-all.

C. The twist is...

1. Things are not what they seem — everything has a magical power.
2. The story is set in the future.
3. Everything is made of candy and sweets!
4. You're in a comic world where everything is drawn, only you are real.
5. Everyone but you talks in rhyme.
6. The story is set in the past.

Turn to page 87 to find your Zodiac Story Cards!

THE ZODIAC STORY PLANNER

Fill in your outcomes to keep track of your story!

A. My story setting is

B. My character is

C. The twist is

My Zodiac Card plot twists are
1.
2.
3.

My character's personality traits are

Tip!

Think about how your character's strengths and weaknesses can affect your story. For example, if they're loud and outgoing, how will they behave during the boring school lesson?

Lizzie's Word Puzzler!

Solve the clues to find the characters!

1. She says her mum is a Hollywood movie star!
_ _ _ _ _ _ _ _ _ _

2. Her lips are sealed...
_ _ _ _ _ _ _ _ _ _

3. Can you spot this Mighty character?
_ _ _ _ _ _ _ _ _ _

4. The baby of Jacky's furry family!
_ _ _ _ _ _ _ _ _ _

5. Ssshhh — no talking allowed!
_ _ _ _ _ _ _ _ _ _

6. This big sis isn't used to blending in with the crowd!
_ _ _ _ _ _ _ _ _ _

7. He gives the best drawing tips!
_ _ _ _ _ _ _ _ _ _

8. She's got hair that looks good enough to eat!
_ _ _ _ _ _ _ _ _ _

9. She's always looking after her siblings!
_ _ _ _ _ _ _ _ _ _

10. Will you find this historic lookalike?
_ _ _ _ _ _ _ _ _ _

11. Destiny's sister.
_ _ _ _ _ _ _ _ _ _

12. She hides in India's attic.
_ _ _ _ _ _ _ _ _ _

```
H E S B T M Y H S K C
E O I R M T T L U Y A
W N A D T U Q O I C T
U C V E O N J O I Z R
Y G H M B J F S F R E
E D P J A C K S O N A
I I S I J T E S N U S
Z A S X N S D L L G U
Z D O J L O T T I E R
I U L Q R N I C K L E
L Y F T S W W J F W Y
L Q U K X C E F Y T C
O F Y T R A M R U Z H
```

Bonus point: Can you find a foundling in there too?

Cut & Create!

Get ready for some snip and stick fun and games!

FABULOUS FAIRIES!

Use these pretty cake toppers to decorate the toadstool cupcakes from page 22.

- Stick this page to card — an old cereal box is perfect.
- Stick some pretty paper to the back to cover the card.
- Now cut out the fairies and decorate your cakes. Sweet!

Turn over to find Tracy B's Do or Discuss cards!

Do or Discuss!

Say bye, bye to boredom with this fun game!

Cut out the cards and pop them in a bowl. Pick one at random then choose to chat with your friends or do an activity.

Do It!

felt tips

Send a picture to Team JW at jwmag@dcthomson.co.uk

Do It!

Dress up as your fave JW character.

PICK ME!

Do It!

Send a funny postcard to your BF — everyone loves a letter!

Do It!

Get tidy — attack your desk, wardrobe or your whole room!

Do It!
Learn to spell 20 new words.

Cacophony

Tiresome

Alternative

Majestic

Do It!

Take a silly selfie!

Do It!
Take a shelfie — you in front of all your books!

Ballet Shoes by Noel Streatfeild
The Children from One End Street by Eve Garnett
The Railway Children by E. Nesbit
Little Women by Louisa M Alcott
A Little Princess by Frances Hodgson Burnett
What Katy Did by Susan Coolidge
Mary Poppins by P.L. Travers
Marianne Dreams by Catherine Storr
The Diary of Anne Frank by Anne Frank
I Capture The Castle by Dodie Smith

Do It!
Sketch a picture of your BF or your pet.

GRRR!

Do It!
Write a new ending for your fave book.

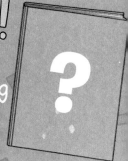
?

Do It!
Try out some cute nail art. Turn to page 40 for a Lucky Dice idea!

Do It!
Write a review for the last book you read — it doesn't have to be a JW book!

Do It!
Draw your BF or your pet Nick Sharratt-style

Do It!
Design some new jewellery for Jacky!

Do It!
Make a list of all the JW books you still have to read.

Do It!
Make or bake something from this book!

JACQUELINE WILSON

Do or Discuss!

Say bye, bye to boredom with this fun game!

Discuss...
The song you'd sing for an X Factor audition.

Discuss...
The best book you've ever read.

Discuss...
The worst book you've ever read.

Discuss...
What you would spend your last £5 on.

Discuss...
Whether you'd rather be Jacqueline Wilson or Nick Sharratt.

Discuss...
A dream you can remember really clearly.

Discuss...
Things that make you laugh.

Discuss...
The best party or special event you've been to.

Discuss...
The job you'd like when you're older.

Discuss...
What your dream house would look like.

Discuss...
Something you'd love to find — like Roman coins or an abandoned puppy!

Discuss...
Things you're scared of.

Discuss...
What you like best about school.

Discuss...
Your most treasured possession.

Discuss...
Your favourite JW book and why you like it.

Aquarius

Write about a treasured possession or a person who means a lot to you.

Pisces

Someone gives you a strange and unusual gift.

Aries
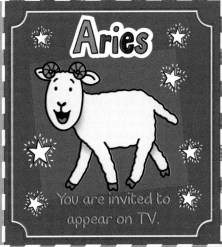
You are invited to appear on TV.

Taurus
You save someone from a very dangerous situation.

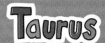

Gemini

Write a fabulous party into your tale.

Cancer
You lose something you were asked to take special care of.

Leo

Write an animal into your story.

Virgo

Someone in the story is a very bad influence!

Libra
You find something very rare and valuable.

Scorpio

You can see into the future when you dream.

Sagittarius

Your story needs a sneaky and spiteful bully!

Capricorn
There is a terrible accident!

 **Aries**

YOUR STORY CHARACTER IS
Funny
Clever
Inventive
One of a kind

BUT ALSO
Stubborn
Cheeky
Snooty
Rebellious

 **Pisces**

YOUR STORY CHARACTER IS
Creative
Loyal
Imaginative
A great friend

BUT ALSO
A day dreamer
Touchy
Lazy
A cry baby

 **Aquarius**

YOUR STORY CHARACTER IS
Generous
Courageous
Enthusiastic
A leader

BUT ALSO
Impatient
Moody
Quick tempered (tantrum alert!)
Impulsive

 **Cancer**

YOUR STORY CHARACTER IS
Caring
Home–loving
Creative
Forward–thinking

BUT ALSO
Moody (Queen of the sulks!)
Clingy
Unpredictable
Mistrustful

 **Gemini**

YOUR STORY CHARACTER IS
Energetic
Adaptable
Amusing
Talented

BUT ALSO
Sneaky
Restless
Frivolous
Hesitant

Taurus

YOUR STORY CHARACTER IS
Generous
Persistent
Patient
Dependable

BUT ALSO
Self–indulgent
Over–sensitive
Lazy
Secretive

Libra

YOUR STORY CHARACTER IS
Graceful
Friendly
Peaceful
Polite

BUT ALSO
Vain
Indecisive
Silly
Irresponsible

Virgo

YOUR STORY CHARACTER IS
Helpful
Reliable
Observant
Precise

BUT ALSO
Fussy
Cold
Interfering
Suspicious

Leo

YOUR STORY CHARACTER IS
Confident
Ambitious
Encouraging
Loyal

BUT ALSO
Bossy
Dramatic
Pompous
Boastful

Capricorn

YOUR STORY CHARACTER IS
Ambitious
Intelligent
Responsible
Trustworthy

BUT ALSO
Penny–pinching
Mistrustful
Overbearing
Mysterious

Sagittarius

YOUR STORY CHARACTER IS
Independent
Positive
Adventurous
Chatty

BUT ALSO
Unemotional
To the point
Disorganised
Easily bored

Scorpio

YOUR STORY CHARACTER IS
Inventive
Creative
Lively
Enthusiastic

BUT ALSO
Jealous
Stubborn
Sly
Obsessive

T-SHIRT TEMPLATES!

Use these templates to make the t-shirt designs on page 42.

Trace the designs on to paper then use the patterns to cut pieces from felt.

POW!

Trace round the letters and cut them from black!

POW!

Trace to this line to cut the yellow flash!

Enlarge this pattern on a photocopier if you want the design to go right across your t-shirt like Marty's.

Trace to the outer line to cut the blue flash!

T-SHIRT TEMPLATES!

FORTUNE FINDER!

Use my portentous plot planner to pick a daring twist for your Victorian story from page 68.

from page 68.

What to do:

Place a pencil in the centre of the circle and give it a spin to find your plot point.

A wealthy family offers your character a fantastic new home, but it means leaving all their old friends behind. Will they accept?

There's a robbery — but your character is blamed! Can they track down the real thief before it's too late?

Your character has to go to hospital after having an accident. Will they recover? Who comes to visit them?

A terrible fire burns down your character's home. Will everyone survive? What will happen afterwards?

An old chest is discovered in an attic and a pile of old love letters is found inside. Will your character track down the sender?

Someone discovers your character's big secret. What is it and how will they react to someone learning it?

A mystery benefactor dies and leaves your character something unexpected in their will. What is it?

A character runs away. What are they running away from and where are they going?

An argument breaks out causing someone to storm off in a huff. What happens next?

Objects are mysteriously moved about during the night with no explanation. Could it be a ghost — or an intruder?

You now have a plot point for your Victorian story. Add it to all your other elements and write a story filled with twists and turns. It's up to you to decide if it will have a happy ending — or not! Don't forget to send your finished stories to jwmag@dcthomson.co.uk!

93

If you loved this annual... you'll love

The Official Jacqueline Wilson Mag

Every issue is packed with cool things to do!

Make and bake awesome stuff!

WIN! AMAZING PRIZES!

I'll reveal my secrets!

WRITE WITH JACKY!

SKETCH WITH NICK!

I'll show you how!

Find out about Jacky's pets...

...and your favourite characters!

That means ME!

And me!

READ ★ WRITE ★ CREATE